Struggling to Breathe:
The Diary of a Psychiatric In-patient

Struggling to Breathe:
The Diary of a Psychiatric In-patient

Niamh Brownlee

Beyond the Pale Books

First published November 2022

BTP Books Ltd

Teach Basil

2 Hannahstown Hill

Belfast BT17 0LT

www.beyondthepalebooks.com

ISBN 978-1-914318-20-7 (Pbk)

Printed in Belfast by GPS Colour

Cover photo: Jemma McCoy

Dedicated to anyone who has lost their life to depression,
their loved ones and everyone who is still fighting.

Sometimes even to live is an act of courage.
Seneca

Author's note:

Any proceeds I receive from the sale of this book will be split between two charities: AWARE NI and Eating Disorders Association NI, as a small thank you for everything they have done for me and my recovery.

Contents

Foreword

AWARE NI

After being discharged from hospital with newfound determination and growing acceptance of her mental health diagnosis, Niamh Brownlee shares her powerful and raw account of depression five years on. Having spent thirty-one days as a mental health in-patient, Niamh has unique insight into what it is like for someone living with severe mental illness. As a young woman aged just twenty-four, the journey is difficult. One filled with fear, guilt and shame, yet interspersed with hope, recognition and gratitude.

As the Depression Charity for Northern Ireland, AWARE recognises the challenges of living with depression and anxiety: how it can affect your relationships, your physical health, and your view of yourself and the world around you. Niamh's story illustrates the exhausting and sometimes all-consuming nature of mental illness, as well as the prolific stigma that increases isolation even further. By utilising local mental health services, including AWARE's Support Groups and wellbeing programmes, we're glad to have seen how Niamh has taken massive steps to equip herself with the knowledge and coping mechanisms to help manage her mental health.

Niamh's eagerness to share her experience to help others aligns with our mission to increase the public understanding of depression, reduce the stigma surrounding the illness and create a future where everyone can openly talk about their mental health.

Niamh's story demonstrates that although recovery is rarely linear, you are never alone, and that there is help, there is hope.

Karen Collins
CEO at AWARE NI

Eating Disorders Association NI

The Eating Disorders Association Northern Ireland (EDA NI) is a peer-led charity that delivers peer support, education and campaigning services for people affected by eating disorders including sufferers, carers and the wider community.

Struggling to Breathe: The Diary of a Psychiatric In-patient is a brave and forthright account of Niamh's experience. We hope her recollection increases public awareness and understanding of mental illness and in-patient care.

If you are struggling with eating distress or would like more information, you are welcome to reach out to EDA NI. Our contact information is below. All the charity's services are free and confidential, and a diagnosis is not required.

You are not alone and recovery from an eating disorder is always possible.

EDA NI 24 Hour Helpline: 028 9023 5959

EDA NI Email: info@eatingdisordersni.co.uk

EDA NI Website: www.eatingdisordersni.co.uk

Health Warning

Please be aware that there is discussion throughout the book of depression, self-harm, suicide and eating disorders, which you may find upsetting. If this is something you are currently dealing with, you might want to wait until you are in a better place before reading on. The book will still be here when you feel better. If you need support, please reach out to those around you if you can and seek help from a medical professional or contact one of the following charities:

AWARE NI Website: www.aware-ni.org

Email: info@aware-ni.org

Eating Disorders Association NI Helpline: 028 9023 5959

If you are in crisis please phone:

Lifeline: 0800 808 8000

Samaritans: 116 123

Emergency Services: 999

Preface

Mental illness was something that crept up on me very slowly over many years, so slowly in fact that it took a long time for me to realise that there was something wrong. By that point I felt unable to speak to anyone around me about the difficulties I was having, and about how serious things had become. I'd convinced myself that the only way to end the torture happening in my head was to die, which is what led to me being admitted to a psychiatric hospital five years ago when I was twenty-four.

This is the diary I kept during that difficult time. Everything is written from my own point of view and true to my own memory, but it's important to note that events, memories and interactions may have been manipulated through the lens of the illness. The names of any patients or hospital staff mentioned throughout the book as well as certain details about them have been changed to protect their identities.

My diary became my main point of contact in the hospital as there were very few people to speak to day-to-day, and I didn't feel able to speak to the family I had around me. In an attempt to make sense of what was happening in my head and my new environment, I started to write down as much as I could. It became one of the only things I could do every day that helped me to feel safe or calm for a short period of time. It also allowed me the space to try to untangle the mess inside my head. The emotions I felt were so powerful that it felt easy for me to tap right back into the moments if the first chance I had to write about something was shortly after, when I was on my own.

There are a few reasons I decided to release this personal account. The first is in the hope that any person living through something similar might feel less alone and see that no matter how awful things seem, help is out there and you can recover. If even one person could feel seen or understood from reading my experience then everything will have been worth it. I also hope that if there are carers of those suffering with mental illness, that they might get an insight into what that person could be going through and see how important their support is, even if it doesn't always seem like it's appreciated at the time.

And lastly, a doctor friend of mine specialising in psychiatry informed me that during their course they study a book written by a psychiatric patient in the 1950s for insight into the patient's experience. I couldn't believe that such an outdated text was being used to teach and train medical staff today and so I hope that my own book will offer a more recent insight. The lack of care and support I and the other patients received was shocking to me but I hope that this could change, and that this account might start a conversation into how we can better support some of the most vulnerable in our society when they need it most.

Finally, I know that parts of what you're about to read may be difficult and things at times seem bleak, but ultimately this is a story of recovery and a reminder that there is always hope. It's important to know that there was light at the end of the tunnel for me and before I even realised it myself, recovery was closer than I thought.

During the time of this diary I could never have imagined my life today. I am so relieved that I am here to share this with you.

Niamh

Day 1

What Have I Done?

How has it got to this? What have I done?

I'm in my little cell perched on the edge of the hard plastic bed. Afraid to touch anything, I can only cry. I'm numb to the tears falling from my face – it's as natural as breathing now. In fact, often it's the easier of the two.

The nurses go through my cluelessly packed case and although they murmur that they're listing each item in case anything goes missing, I know they're rating each item as a method of suicide. Oh, God. This is so wrong. I'm terrified. How has this happened?

I get a tour of the psychiatric ward. It's one big circle. The women have private rooms while the men are only separated by a curtain between them. This is the over-sixty-fives ward; at twenty-four years old I'm not supposed to be here but it was the only place with a bed available in Northern Ireland. I'm grateful they had a spot. I think. A few hours ago I didn't even know this was an option. As I told the nurse in my living room before coming here, I knew exactly what I was going to do. I had it all planned out. She gave me this alternative as a lifeline: a chance to get away somewhere safe, away from temptation and danger. I'm afraid and sick with guilt, but I'm here.

I send my mum away after fifteen minutes alone together. Her sterling enthusiasm of the view from the window and how lucky I am to have a sink in the room is exhausting and I'm so far beyond pleasantries right now. I'm afraid to be alone here but I also need her to go. The hurt on her face when I tell her she can leave is like a punch in the heart and a slap across the face, but how can she stay when she's part of the problem? I hate how horrible I've become. I don't deserve anyone around me.

To be fair to her she takes it on the chin and leaves with gusto, although I know that, like me, she's putting on a brave face. I can see she's scared to leave me here and I almost call her back to stay, but the door closes and the moment it does I'm crying again.

This time, on my own, I allow myself to sob and heave and grip the side of the bed until my knuckles are stretched and white and I can't breathe and I'm having one of the worst panic attacks of my life and everything bad and ugly and poisonous is in me and has filled my lungs, and I think – how have you let it get to this! Look what you're putting everyone through! Again I curse myself for being such a selfish person. If I was dead, I wouldn't be doing this to anyone and this would all be over.

The first few hours are a blur of nurses coming in and out of the room introducing themselves and asking how I am. Thank Christ none of them are *actually* asking. I'm too exhausted after today's events to talk anymore. I think I'm maybe in shock too. They tell me that because it's Friday afternoon I won't be seen by a doctor until Monday, so I should 'hang tight, relax and settle in' for the next few days. They make it sound like some sort of retreat, but I can't shake the feelings of utter shame and repulsion at myself for allowing things to go this far. I never, ever meant to end up here.

For the rest of my life I will have to live with being admitted to this ward for my own safety. What if anyone finds out? I'm petrified at the thought of anyone in the world outside my mum and dad and brother and auntie knowing I'm here. Even them knowing is too much. How must they be feeling? If I had gone through with my plan, I wouldn't be here and this wouldn't be happening. That would have been better for everyone.

I have nothing to do, so I unpack my clothes and hang them in the wardrobe. Gone are the days when I wore anything remotely attractive or anything that gave a hint of a shape underneath, and I wonder if the flimsy plastic hangers will hold my XL jumpers. The bar holding the hangers starts to bow slightly under the weight of my few items of clothes. I realise it's built to break with any weight at all. Like a body.

The first night is awful. I've never experienced a loneliness like this as the realisation of what has happened hits me hard. I am the people I was always scared of – insane and imprisoned in hospital. Do they still have straitjackets and padded rooms? What if they decide I'm too mad and I never leave again? I think of the book *One Flew over the Cuckoo's Nest* and I think, shit – are they going to give me electric-shock treatment to fry me back to sense, or remove part of my brain? Does that still happen? My whole life feels out of control; like I no longer have any say whatsoever in what happens to me. Should I lie to the doctors and nurses that I am better so they'll let me out? But if they do, I know I'll find a way to kill myself. I'm torn between making that happen and being scared of it.

My heart is racing and my breath struggles to escape my lungs on time. My chest is covered in hot red blotches and sweat drips down the back of my neck. The panic started inside my head but now it's made its way into every part of my body. I'm too weak to shut it down and I know I'm making it worse by allowing my mind to spiral into dark and overwhelming places, but I can't stop. I've passed the point where I can pull it back. This illness has taken over and there's nothing I can do.

I try lying down flat on the bed but the sheets and the blanket and the pillows scratch against my skin and I can't get the thought out of my head that other people have shared this bed. I feel dirty and I put on bottoms tucked into my socks and a long-sleeved jumper with a hood. I wrap my jacket around the pillow to make sure none of my skin is touching hospital material. I keep imagining there are bedbugs running up my arms and legs, so I sit upright on the chair in the corner instead.

A few more hours have passed – it's sometime after 1 a.m., and my thoughts are still torturous and insistent. Mum went to the hospital shop earlier and bought me a few magazines. I've tried to tire myself by flicking through them but my mind is such a mess that I can't concentrate on anything. Our building is kept separate from the rest of the hospital, including the shop, with an entrance to ourselves. We're the farthest away from any other ward. Did they do that on purpose? I move to the window. It can only open an inch from the bottom and I can't get any air. I try to focus on the sounds of the cars outside but they are too loud and aggressive and I imagine them spinning out of control and screeching and crashing into each other. I begin to think that because I have the image in my head, it will actually happen and it will be my fault, so I screw my eyes closed and shake my head violently side to side to get rid of the picture before somebody gets hurt. My breathing gets worse – like there's a ton weight sitting on my chest. I close the window and count the tiles on the ceiling. I can't get past eight or nine without forgetting what number I'm on and needing to restart.

It's now 2.30 a.m. and I still can't sleep. I open the door of my room and the rest of the ward is in complete darkness and deathly silent. It makes the screaming in my head sound louder and I can hear my heart beating so fast I think it could burst. I picture the blood struggling to pump through my veins and I think, my body can't cope. Will I die here? How can no one else hear the screaming that I can? I know it's in my head but it's louder than a drill and an ambulance – surely some of the sound would escape. I don't know what I'm looking for in the corridor, so I go back into the dark room. I'm pacing the three steps that take me wall to wall, trying every second to fend off and swallow the panic that threatens to block my throat and choke me, when a nurse walks past and spots me through the thin window in the door. We make eye contact for a second until I jump out of sight. I'm not sure why. I hide until I think she's gone, but she comes back a minute later, into the room this time. She doesn't say a word but hands me a pill. I whisper to her asking what it is and she tells me it's a sleeping tablet. I've never had one before but I don't question it. I take it with a gulp of water –

nearly choking because my breathing is still erratic. I manage to swallow and then wrap myself in my clothes again and lie back down on a corner of the bed.

After an hour it still hasn't worked. I'm wide awake and demented. I go to the nurse and ask if she can give me another one. I stand at the door of the nurses' office in my pyjamas with red eyes and my chest heaving. Hopefully she can see from the dark circles around my eyes and the tenseness of my body that I haven't slept properly in weeks. Thankfully she doesn't ask what's wrong; she doesn't ask if I'm okay or if I want to talk about it. She hands over another pill and watches me swallow it. I'm annoying her being awake at this hour when she had probably hoped for a quiet shift. I can tell from the silence that not one of the old men or women on the ward is awake; everyone is in a deep sleep. Maybe they've all been given sleeping tablets too.

An hour later, just before it hits 5 a.m., the tablets finally start to work. I become drowsy and my eyes won't stay open. It's a strange sensation: my mind is still working overtime but with what feels like a thick cloud descending over it. I forget why I'm feeling sad and afraid and I'm aware that my brain is starting to hush. The numbness it's bringing is like a big warm blanket wrapping round me and there's relief as everything goes quiet. I have a distant thought while my body succumbs to the numbness – what if I need to pee? Will I be too deep under that I'll wet myself? I'm too drowsy now to care. I know somewhere in my mind that things are bad, but right now I let myself enjoy the feeling of sinking into black.

Day 2

Breakfast Inside

I'm woken by a nurse knocking at 8 a.m. She pokes her head round my door and tells me it's breakfast time. I stare at her for a while before I process what she's said and tell her okay. My brain is so slow lately (and it probably doesn't help that the sleeping tablets are continuing to work their way through my system). I can hear what people say but it's almost as if it needs translated in my brain before I can form a response and tell my mouth to go. It's exhausting and embarrassing and means I usually don't bother trying to talk to anyone.

I look out into the hallway, covered in my protective layers of clothes from the night before, and see the other patients, frail and stooped, shuffling *en masse* round the corner and out of sight. It's the first time I've seen them in daylight. I didn't think over sixty-five sounded that old but these people are so thin and delicate that I'd be scared to brush past any of them. It's then that I realise I'm expected to leave my room and eat alongside the other patients in the dining room the nurses showed me last night. I can't imagine in my head what this will look like.

I tiptoe out of my room when the crowd has passed and it's quiet again and head towards the noise of breakfast. It's only a few doors down from me. I peer round the door, foggy from sleep and the tablets. My socks are still tucked into my pyjamas and I wonder if I was supposed to get dressed, but everyone else is wearing thin, worn dressing gowns. The few women appear completely out of it and don't notice me at all. Some of the old men stare at me – one with cornflakes and milk dripping right down his wrinkly chin and another with no teeth being spoon-fed porridge by a nurse. A skinny little lady in the corner starts to take her clothes off and a nurse runs over and forces them back on her. I'm horrified and hit by a wave of nausea. My head goes light and I blink to try to get rid of the black spots that have appeared in front of my eyes. I'm the youngest person here by at least forty years. I know it's awful but I feel repulsed by these old people.

I'm frozen and don't move a muscle in case someone makes me sit down and join the group. No one speaks but more are noticing me now and stare like I'm a strange animal they've come to see in the zoo. My head spins, making me dizzy and unable to move my feet. I imagine the walls closing in and I think I might faint when one of the nurses sees the panic on my face and tells me I can take a tray to my room to eat 'until I get settled'. Now everyone is staring at me because she's disturbed the awkward quiet of before.

A man takes out his teeth and sets his dentures beside his glass, long lines of saliva following it right onto the table. A woman begins to argue with a nurse, flinging her arms around like a bat, and two other nurses run over to restrain her. Someone passes me a tray. I don't know what's on it and they ask me a question I don't hear. I turn and try to run back to my room but they all look the same – five identical doors in a row, so I choose the one I think is mine and look through the little window. I can see people in there and it looks like an old lady getting a nappy changed by a nurse. I freak out and feel sick and try the next window where I recognise my suitcase. I shut the door behind me and stand with my back against it trying to breathe. I hadn't realised I was holding my breath. What is happening here? I can't do this. I nearly drop my tray – I forgot I was holding it – and place it on the little table with wheels. I'm in a nightmare. I can never, ever eat in that room with everybody. The smell and the sound of people slopping their food about their droopy mouths makes my stomach flip.

I look down at the tray and see there's a tiny amount of cornflakes and milk in a red plastic bowl and a piece of dry white toast on a red plastic plate. I think the nurse had asked if I wanted butter. I'm completely overwhelmed. I push the tray away and get onto the bed. I fall asleep and an hour later when I wake the tray is gone. I'm mortified that someone was in the room as I slept and had to lift my rubbish. The nurses will be talking about me and how rude I am, thinking I expect to be tidied up after.

I've been in hospital only once before, for pneumonia, a few years ago. I stayed for two nights and remember they were keen to get me home again and free up a bed, which I assume will be the same here. I had my own room then too, but the ward was busy and friendly and I actually enjoyed it at the time. I guess I'll be a few nights here – maybe a week at the very most. I'll be kept until they think I'm out of the danger zone and then they'll send me back home. A week feels too long. Making it to the end of the day seems impossible.

I don't know anyone who has been admitted to a psychiatric ward in the last forty years and it's not something that comes up in conversation, so I don't know the normal length of stay. I ask a nurse who comes to take some bloods, but she gives a vague response that it depends on the person and she really can't say. I don't need anything exact, but I need to prepare myself if this will take longer than the weekend. Could I be here for weeks? There's no way it could be a month. Finally, sensing my desperation, one of the senior nurses takes pity on me when she comes to introduce herself and tells me quietly that usually people stay for at least two to three weeks. She looks at me for a long time, waiting for a response, but I don't know what to say. I thought it would shock or upset me – and that's what she was probably waiting for too, but surprisingly I'm actually relieved. I wasn't expecting that.

I unpack the last few things from my suitcase, knowing now that I'll be here a while, and tell myself not to panic, to breathe, and that everything is okay. I repeat that in my head over and over but it doesn't change anything. I try to relax by sitting back against the pillows on my bed and closing my eyes, but my shoulders stay high and tight and tense and my neck feels stiff and sore from trying to hold everything together for so long. My mind continues to zip from thought to thought so quickly I can't keep up and I'm left feeling drained and physically exhausted even though I've barely moved. I can't switch off.

My body is always tense these days because I have to hold myself tightly together to stop from falling apart. My back throbs, my jaw aches from grinding my teeth at night and my head pounds with stress. All of that intensifies after interacting with anybody. I wonder if anyone notices how slow I move and speak around them. Every part of me is exhausted and happy to let go and give up. I feel like my body is switching off and shutting down and I would welcome it except for the screaming, shouting, thrashing voice in my head not allowing me the peace. It shouts so violently I find it unbelievable that no one else can hear it outside of me. I look in the mirror, avoiding eye contact, to check that the screaming is just in my head and that no one else knows what's happening in there. It's hard to be sure because I can't look at myself.

I try to tell myself that I'm safe here, that this is a good place to be, that I can get better here, but I'm not convinced. My whole being remains on edge, ready to fight whatever rational thought tries to be heard over the madness, and that battle in my head leaves my body with zero energy to move. It's like a thick wall has been built between me and recovering from this. I'm scared at what the doctors are going to ask me. I'm not strong enough for anything difficult and there's no more room in my head to deal with painful feelings. What am I trying to protect myself from? What is left that isn't already poisoned and ruined? I'm afraid that if I speak or open up, the screaming and crying and thrashing in my head will make its way out of my mouth and everyone will hear and be disgusted and horrified and lock me away forever. If I open that door at all, I'll never get it closed.

A nurse giving out lunchtime tablets comes to check on me and lets me know that because I've been coming off my previous antidepressant in the last few weeks (it clearly wasn't working) to make way for a new one, and because I haven't seen the doctor yet, she's nothing for me other than another sleeping tablet if I start to panic. I ask for a tablet immediately thinking maybe I can sleep through today. She passes one over and watches me swallow it. Too many of these at once must be dangerous if they always watch me take them.

When she leaves I pat myself on the back for not showing her the extent to which I'm falling apart and struggling to breathe. She wasn't concerned because I was able to speak to her and ask for a tablet and swallow it like a normal person would. Was that wrong? I don't know how to tell her the truth. I know that isn't what I'm here for – I know I should let the mask fall and allow myself to be honest and truthful but I can't do that. I don't know how. I don't know how I'm supposed to act or what I'm supposed to be doing in here. I'm so wired that the tablet has no effect. Next time I'll ask for two.

My mum and auntie visit. Mum must have felt she needed support to face me today. She's taken time off work because I'm in here, but I'm not sure why because there's nothing she can really do for me and when she visits it only takes up ten minutes of her day. I don't know what she's told her work and I'm too scared to ask. They've brought bed sheets and a pillowcase from home. The scratchy questionable stuff from the hospital is bundled up and placed on top of the wardrobe where it still makes my skin crawl but not as much knowing I don't have to surround myself in it anymore.

I'm both embarrassed and glad to see them being practical, fussing and cleaning; helping in the only way they can, but I can't help it or stop when I start to cry. They think it's because of the situation and my current mental breakdown when in fact it's because I want them to leave. It's stressing me out having them here but I can't communicate that. Yesterday none of this was real and I was in a weird dream or nightmare, but having them in here – real-life normal people from outside – makes me see this is actually happening and I'm locked inside here for who knows how long.

I'm also angry at them and frustrated too because they refuse to ask any real questions or talk about why I'm here. They skirt round it and don't mention it even when we're surrounded by the result of it. Maybe they're waiting for me to bring it up, but why should I? I'm supposed to be the sick one, the weak one, the one who wasn't coping in the real world. They don't ask how I am or how I feel; instead they ask about breakfast and talk about the weather outside. My own family is too embarrassed to acknowledge the state of my mental health. Inside I'm begging them to talk to me or help me or at least see I'm here and acknowledge what's happening, but even as I think this I know I wouldn't give them a real answer and they probably know it too, which is why they won't ask. They *have* asked, a long time ago, and had their heads bitten off for mentioning it, so of course they won't try again. For the hundredth time today I'm reminded of the burden I'm putting on everyone. I hate myself.

I'm so agitated with their presence in this tiny room that I can't sit down. Instead I stand by the sink avoiding eye contact like a weirdo. I can't follow the conversation because my head is screaming, 'YOU'RE DISGUSTING. EVERYONE HATES YOU. YOU NEED TO DIE.' Even with my family here, talking to me and distracting me, somehow the voices continue to tell me I'm fat and useless and better off dead.

I need them both to leave now. I don't want anyone seeing me here, especially because I feel another panic attack rising inside me. I can't cope with the truth – that this is all real, and I'm scared and feel so alone, but I also want someone here with me. I'm confused and unable to answer the benign questions they're asking because my head is too loud and I can't stop the angry, frustrated tears running down my face. They try to touch me and I snap at them not to and jump across the room out of reach of their touch like I've been burned. I'm torn because really I would love to be hugged and held but I can't let myself and I don't know why, so instead I act like a brat. Why am I like this? This isn't me. I back into the corner, the farthest I can get away, and beg my thoughts to please, please be quiet for just one minute to let me pull myself together and stop looking such a mess. I hit the side of my head with my fist over and over, trying desperately to knock my thoughts into some order to be able to hold a conversation but I can see this freaks my mum and auntie out further. It probably does look a bit manic. I usually keep this sort of thing to myself but I'm really trying to regain control and my head is so loud that I'd forgotten they're here. I don't want them to see me like this and I really don't want them to worry or be afraid of me. I ask them to leave, saying that I'm not feeling well and I know Mum is scared for me and doesn't know what to do. I see a look of shock and horror on my auntie's face and I realise how mad I must look. Up to now I've always been good at hiding what's happening in my head but this is more than I've ever dealt with before. Finally they leave and I don't move from the corner and can't even look at them when they go because I know I'll cry or shout at them to stay. I watch them from my window, four floors down on the street getting into the car. They turn and wave and even though it's far away, I can see my mum is crying. I get into bed and curl up into a ball. I cry until I sleep.

Day 3

The Nun

A few days ago, when I came into hospital, I had to answer questions and one of them was about religion. I don't know why it's relevant but the nurse asked and I told her I'm a Catholic, even though I haven't been to Mass in years. I do still pray sometimes, usually when I'm at my worst and need help. Anyway, because of that, I think, a tiny little nun came to visit me today. She sat in the hard plastic chair beside the sink while I sat on the bed. She asked how I was and she didn't really say much about God, which I was thankful for, but she did give me the latest bulletin from Mass over in the main hospital building. She wanted to pray with me, which was awkward but I let her, and then she said she would come back with Communion for me in a few days. I didn't have the heart to tell her I was okay without because she was so eager and genuine and had such a calming influence for the short time she was in my room. If I was braver and hadn't been afraid of upsetting her, I would have asked why her God lets things like this happen and why he's doing this to me when I had always tried to be a good person, but she was too sweet and innocent and softly spoken that I couldn't do it. I was also worried she would say I'm being punished for something or had the devil inside me and I don't know what I would say to that (although I suppose it would be nice to have a reason for all this). She leaves after a while but her smell of talcum powder and sweet perfume lingers.

I remember a year or two ago Mum paying for me to have a one-off assessment with a private psychiatrist at the recommendation of our family GP who 'didn't know what to do with me'. At the end of our ninety-minute session (and Mum less £350) he told me that alongside high-intensity exercise and mindfulness I should try to 'get into God'. He said lots of his mental health patients found comfort in religion and I remember thinking it seemed like a strange thing to prescribe: meditate, go for a run and pray. What a waste of money that was!

Today's lunch is yellow and indistinguishable. There are textures I've never experienced. I think it's custard with roast potatoes. There's something fried as well with, I think, vegetables in it. I can definitely see a pea. A few hours later the fried thing is for dinner too, but there's nothing else to do in the day, so I eat it. It doesn't taste too awful, even though I'm still not sure what it is.

The strange lukewarm food being served at every meal has given me the runs, unfortunately, and having to share a bathroom with thirteen very old, very slow pensioners makes for an uncomfortable situation. That I want to hide in my room all day long and not make eye contact with anyone doesn't help because the bathroom is at the other end of the corridor, but because I have to go more than usual right now as my stomach gets to grips with this new food, I move quickly with my head down and hover over the toilet seat until my thighs burn. I can't let myself sit on the same toilet the old bums have been on. I might have to start making a toilet-paper cover each time I need to wee to shield me from germs. I'm scared I'll sit down on the loo and it'll be warm – ugh! I also try not to look at anything too closely in case I see any old people hairs or wee. It reminds me of the bathroom in my granny's house because it's covered in disabled handrails and emergency cords hanging from the ceiling.

A few nurses pop in and out of my room to take bloods or notes and I make absolutely no effort with them and have no intention of remembering any of their names. I used to be such a nice smiley person but I don't have the energy or motivation anymore. Sensing my discomfort, they tell me it will take a while for me to settle in and make myself comfortable 'until I get better'. I obviously haven't told them this but I've decided over the last few horrible days that I've no intention of settling in or getting comfortable or of even getting better. The only way I can see out of this is to die. It's a scary idea but it quiets my thoughts when I think that the noise in my head could actually stop. I would do anything for that. It's just a question of when exactly, and how. I'm okay to sit with it for another couple of days.

I think there's a communal TV in the men's section of the ward that's on during the day but I could never go and sit there with the others. I had been spending eighty per cent of the day sleeping at home but it's too noisy and bright and uncomfortable here for me to escape into sleep. Mum was desperate to buy me my own iPad – I could tell she thought it might go some way towards making me happy, or maybe it was her way of apologising for something (if only it was that easy), but I didn't let her. Instead, my auntie lent me her iPad and has given me her Netflix password to help pass the long days in here.

It has been so long now, weeks or maybe even months, since I watched the TV or a movie or went to the cinema. It might look like I'm watching because my eyes are on the screen but I'm not able to listen or take anything in. I've been too distracted and agitated and unable to sit down for longer than ten or fifteen minutes. It feels like there's always something gnawing away in the back of my mind – like I've forgotten something important or I'm waiting for something bad to happen but I don't know what it is. It's too hard to concentrate when my brain is shouting awful things at me and I can't hear what anyone on the screen is saying. Sometimes I can strain over the noise to hear the TV but it only lasts a second before the volume on my thoughts turns up as if to say there's no point in trying to get away from this. It's exhausting and I usually sleep instead to get a break.

I flick through the shows and series and movies on the iPad, overwhelmed by the number of options, and eventually settle on a romcom I've seen before. I get about twenty minutes in before getting restless and put on an episode of *Gilmore Girls* instead. It's nearly over when I snap back to life and realise I haven't actually watched any of it. I've been staring into space.

A memory slips into my head – it must be the extra time and space I have in here to think. I remember when I was about seven or eight I used to get a tummy ache. I noticed that it usually happened just before something bad occurred – like a fight at home or falling out with a friend in school. I started to believe I could predict bad things happening when my stomach got sore. I could be having a good day at school but if my stomach then hurt, I knew something awful was coming to ruin my day. And when the stomach pains started, I got ready: I clenched my fists and was on high alert waiting for this awful thing to happen. Usually something bad did happen, but that was probably because I was looking so hard for it. I didn't tell anyone about my sore stomachs because I didn't want anyone to laugh at me or think I was mad. I maybe didn't have the words to explain it then either. Looking back and comparing that to where I am today, it must have been the start of some form of anxiety. I was worrying myself sick over something that didn't even exist. I must have been a really weird kid.

Day 4

Meeting the Doctor

Finally, after the longest weekend that went on forever, I get to meet the doctor. I'm called as I leave my breakfast tray round to the kitchen and go straight to the consultation room with a nurse. I rattle off my life story to the two of them from childhood up until a week ago for what must be the fifteenth or sixteenth time by now because I never see the same person twice. I should write it down and print a few copies to pass to every new person who seems to need to hear it first-hand, even though it must be in my notes somewhere. Do they not realise how uncomfortable and traumatic it is each time – telling complete strangers I've known for a few minutes my most painful memories and darkest, worst thoughts about myself?

It's difficult and emotional but I don't let the doctor see me cry. This time, although unpleasant, I try to get through without attaching anything I'm saying to myself; I pretend to tell someone else's story. I just want to get to the end so I can stop talking and let the doctor tell me what he's going to do. He doesn't interrupt, so I speak unprompted and finish with 'and then I came here'. He stares at me for a while, makes some notes and then starts with the questions.

I've answered these so many times now that I could go through the doctor's script myself: 'Do you hear voices

speaking in your head that aren't your own?' No, it's always
my voice. 'Do you ever hear messages from the radio or TV?'
No, again, which rules out schizophrenia. 'Have you ever
been sexually abused? Physically abused?' God, thankfully
not. 'Can you think of anything that makes you happy?' Not
at the minute. Maybe my dog.

'Is life worth living?'

There it is. The only question that really matters. I often
wonder why they ask that question last when to me it says
way more than any of the others. I think carefully about my
response for a while before answering, really trying this time
to search inside and rattle around every corner of my head
for anything that makes life worthy of staying alive. I picture
my dog's happy face and get a surge of guilt. Like so many
times before when this question has been asked, I hate myself
for the answer. I wish I could lie because I feel like I've failed
when I'm honest and answer, 'No.'

I realise I must be getting better at reliving everything; my
voice barely wobbles this time and only a tiny lump forms in
my throat. I'm becoming numb to it. Maybe I'm protecting
myself because I can't face any more upset right now. The
doctor may ask the questions but it's me who has to go back
to my room alone afterwards and think about everything he's
made me say. It's difficult but I always do it anyway – tell
the many doctors over the years about vomiting up meals or
crashing the car, in the hope they'll offer some magic insight
or a way out of this.

He's stopped talking so I look up at him and the nurse. I
don't think they believe anything I've said. They think I'm
putting this on – why would anyone do that? I try to imagine
what they see and hear as they interview me and I worry that
when I leave they'll turn to each other and decide there's
nothing wrong with me – I'm hormonal, overemotional or
overthinking everything, something everyone does at times,
and send me home. That scares me because although I don't
want to be here, I don't know anywhere else I want to be either.

The problem is they didn't know me before. They didn't see how I used to be before my brain was taken over and I lost control of my thoughts. They wouldn't believe me if I told them I used to be fun and kind and happy and enthusiastic and full of life and normal – even better than normal. I swear, at times I used to be the loudest, most confident person in the room. Even I can hardly believe it. I try to see myself through their eyes, sitting here in my grey extra-large jumper and baggy trousers with my hair hanging round my face in an effort to try and hide. I imagine I look like a big mound of clay that's started to melt in the sun. A grey, lifeless shape of a person who is cold and rude to the people she cares about and cries all the time alone in bed and can't remember what it feels like to laugh or smile.

The doctor tells me what he's going to do next (spoiler: not much), and I'm annoyed at myself for once again getting my hopes up. Even more annoying, my eyes involuntarily begin to water and I have to fight not to let the tears spill over. I hate angry tears.

He names a new antidepressant for me to start. He says that so far I've been 'treatment-resistant' which means the medications haven't worked. It's true, but it makes me feel like I've been doing something wrong. That's it. No feedback, no insight, no pearls of wisdom or words of support. I had hoped for a better outcome. After waiting anxiously for the doctor and his verdict all weekend, I had nearly convinced myself that this would be the turning point. I'm in hospital, where people come to get better, and this doctor is an expert and committed and knows what to do. Things might even begin to change. In my desperation I had tricked myself that this was where the ball would start rolling – that something would happen or someone would make a suggestion that would make me better and I could start to recover. I had a crazy idea that the doctor would say yes, he could fix me. Or that I was worthy of being saved.

But after once again pouring my heart out I can see that he doesn't understand, he doesn't know what to do, he has no plan for this. Alongside the shiny new antidepressant and an anti-anxiety tablet, he says I can have up to three sleeping tablets a day. Lucky me. He's looking at me for a response but I can't give him one. There's a silent furious tear creeping down my cheek that we're both aware of but don't mention.

I realise now that this is the most that's going to happen and I think, there it is. No one can help. No one knows what to do. They might listen if you're lucky, but no one has a clue how to make things better. This is probably the seventh or eighth doctor I've met with now who prescribes medication and nothing else. It confirms what I already know but what the last glimmers of hope had been keeping at bay: no one gives a shit. It doesn't matter if I'm alive or dead. I'm a nuisance in this doctor's day.

I'm attempting to scrape myself up off the sofa to leave when the doctor asks why I'm crying. I gulp out that I don't mean to be rude but I was just hoping for something more, that I hoped he might have suggested something to help. He asks what *I* think could help. This sets me off again and I'm fully crying now, still standing with one hand on the door, but this time the tears I can't stop are out of frustration. 'That's why I'm here!' I want to shout. 'This is *your* job, not mine. You're supposed to help me. I don't know what I need!' But instead I croak out through the sobs that I don't know what could help. He looks at me with disgust and disappointment. I'm mortified at the state I'm in, so I leave and shuffle back to my room filled with self-loathing, telling myself what a pathetic, stupid mess I am.

Back in my room I remember each horrible experience I've had with healthcare professionals since this whole sorry saga began. One stands out from about a year ago when a nurse told me, 'maybe you're just not a happy person'. God, I still think about that a few times a week and it makes my insides contract when I do. It was one of the worst things she could have said. I spent days, weeks, thinking maybe she was right, that I'm a negative sad loser and I don't have an illness at all. It made me think I'd have to learn to live with this new way of life. Other times I felt angry and had fierce arguments in my head where I stood up to her and said she was wrong – that I definitely wasn't always like this and this is not who I am. But even in my head she always won.

I think she was wrong, though. My real self, before it was taken over by this depression, wasn't negative or cynical or unmotivated. In fact, I swear I was the opposite. I used to be brave and silly and carefree and confident and fun and enthusiastic and full of life and I could relax and unwind. I had almost too many hobbies and interests and so many friends I didn't know what to do with them. I had dreams and plans for the future. Cheesy and embarrassing as it sounds, I remember a time when I thought I could change the world. I wanted to travel to every country, build a school to teach in in Africa, look after sick animals in Asia, walk the Great Wall of China and swim the Great Barrier Reef. Now it's hard to believe I thought I could achieve any of that. Bit by bit I picked apart each of my dreams and thought myself out of them.

I'm not brave enough.

Not smart enough or able.

I could never do anything brilliant.

Everyone else is better than me.

I'm too fat and ugly to achieve anything worthwhile.

No one really likes me. How could they?

Telling myself those words over and over on a loop inside my head, becoming more aggressive each time, I started to believe it all very quickly. And then one day every area of my life was tainted with the same dark thoughts and I couldn't even get up in the morning without thinking what a waste of space I was. The thought of ever building a school or travelling the world now fills me with anxiety and panic and makes me want to hide under the duvet and sleep forever. I can't believe what I've become.

My mind, my outlook and my personality are tainted by depression. It's completely changed who I am. I hate myself. I

feel worthless. Depression has made me believe that everyone
else feels the same way about me too. I'm ashamed to say that
it's winning; it's in control, it's choking me and starving me
of air and life and it looks like there's no one who can help.
What a cruel thing it is. It exhausts you completely so you
can't fight back. I know I need help if I'm to get better, but
where? I thought it would be here. Maybe the doctors see that
it's been too many years of constant hate and abuse towards
myself and they know it's too late. Maybe it's not possible to
undo the damage I've done.

I see my depression most clearly when I compare myself to
what I used to be and I realise what it has robbed me of. It's
made me push everyone away and isolate myself. It has made
me terrified of everything and given me an unrelenting self-
hatred. It has convinced me to give up. I know I shouldn't be
sitting here alone and crying in a dirty hospital room at the age
of twenty-four – this was never part of the plan, but depression
somehow latched on, clung to me when I was vulnerable. I can
see now I was an easy target; always pushing myself harder and
harder, a fierce critic when I was anything less than perfect,
unable to admit to anyone that anything was ever wrong.

But it doesn't matter how I got here because it doesn't help
me move forward. I'm in too deep now and I don't know
how to separate myself from it. The guilt and shame that I've
let this happen is enough to crush me. I should have been
stronger and able to fight it.

My biggest fear, and I suppose what has allowed this
depression to grow and survive in me for so long, is that if I
open my mouth, it could spread into my friends and family and
take them over too; as if by talking about it and telling people
my thoughts, depression will find a way to leak out of me and
poison the minds of everyone around me. What if I finally
open up and everyone begins to see the world how I see it or
starts to think how I think? That's why I've kept it a secret, for
fear of it spreading. I hoped that if I kept pushing it away and
pretending I was fine it would eventually disappear. But instead

I've let it flourish and I've hurt everyone I love anyway.

I'm getting dressed in my room and coming to terms with feeling like I'm really on my own in this when, sensing someone's eyes on me, I turn to find the face of a little woman older than life itself pressed right up against the window in the door. I nearly jump out of my skin when she starts shouting 'Jennifer! Jennifer!' at me and I stare wide-eyed and horrified at her until, thank God, one of the nurses escorts her back to her room.

I breathe again and find myself almost laughing at the ridiculousness of this whole situation and where I am. If anyone from the outside saw me now! I place a towel over my door to block the window while I change, but within minutes one of the nurses comes to check on me and I realise the window is there for a reason. How come no one is about when I'm in hysterics and convulsions of panic on my bed but straight over when I'm changing?

A social worker and benefits lady come to see me in the afternoon to talk about what I can apply for and what I'm entitled to claim now that I'm 'officially' sick and not able to work. They come at the same time Mum arrives but I don't want to miss them because I've been waiting for something interesting to happen, so they come into the room while Mum fusses around with the bedclothes and gives the floor a brush. I don't mind initially that they're all here, thinking that we'll only be talking about money and the dole, but it turns out they ask me if I've ever attempted suicide and if so, how many times. I make a face at them and then at Mum, whose back is turned. They nod and move on.

In a weird moment of madness before bed I decide to download the Instagram app on my auntie's iPad and make an account. I've got this thought in my head tonight that seeing as it looks like nothing positive is going to come out of this experience, I'm going to try and make something good happen while I'm in this situation. I find Ed Sheeran's Instagram and go to his latest picture. I start typing out a message under the post saying how I'm in a psychiatric ward and his music has been helping me to feel like there's hope. This is all a lie; I *used* to love listening to his music, but I don't love anything anymore. I'm really just thinking that maybe he'll see the message in between the other thousands and decide to take pity on me and offer me free VIP tickets to his next concert. At least that might give me something to look forward to. But after typing the message out and rereading it, I start to worry that someone I know might see it and then everyone would find out where I am. I delete the message and uninstall the app. It was stupid anyway.

Day 5

My Depression

It's always quiet here. I know that means it should be peaceful but somehow it's the opposite. My head is chaotic and I can hardly get a breath between the shouts and cries and screams between my ears.

Lying on my bed with nothing to distract me I imagine I'm becoming invisible, that there is nothing left of me. My body is the empty shell that remains, following orders and staring blankly at the world and everyone in it. I've finally given up the fight and the pretence. I don't have the energy or the will to try any longer.

I have time to think about what led to me being here and how this happened. I've nowhere to go and empty hours to fill and it gets harder and harder to ignore the thoughts and memories pushing up against my consciousness. I know this has been a long time coming and that my mental state has been in decline for a while. It was three years ago almost exactly that I first went to my GP and told her how sad I felt and that I spent each day thinking how much I wanted to die and the amazing relief it would be if I did. I told her I made myself sick every other day too.

My mum was there for the start of the conversation (she was the one who made me admit that any of this was happening and got me the appointment), but I had to ask her to leave when she started silently crying because then I couldn't get the words out. It was just a few days earlier that she'd come to my room where I was sitting on my laptop desperately trying to work. I'd been in this position for months and was getting nowhere. University deadlines were piling up on top of me, only making it more difficult to concentrate and get anything done. She asked something simple like did I want any dinner and I bit her head off and was horrible to her. She snapped at me then, rightly so, and said, 'This is not normal. What is wrong with you?' She was ready for a screaming match but I started to cry. She asked if I was okay and I said no. She asked if I thought I was depressed and I said yes. She said it was okay and they would get me help. She said she knew something was up and she wished she'd asked sooner. She asked if I would ever do anything bad and I said yes, I tried to crash the car a few days ago. I knew she was horrified but she tried to stay calm. She asked if there was anything else and I said I made myself sick a lot. She said she had suspected something like that was going on. I asked her to go, which she did, but she tried to hug me and I couldn't take it, shrugging her off to go back to my coursework.

I was in shock then and couldn't believe I'd said the bad things out loud. This was real now. I had had the realisation for myself lying alone in bed about six months before. I was depressed. But I told myself that I would never tell anyone and it would go away on its own. I let myself believe that when university was over it would go away – or if not then, when I got a job. Or maybe when I moved out. Or maybe when I lost two stone. But instead it got worse. It festered in my mind, this secret with myself. I stopped doing anything for fun. I stopped going on nights out with my friends, always making up excuses. I stopped meeting up with people for lunch or coffee. I stopped hanging out with my group of girls between lectures, sitting in silence on my own in the car while telling everyone I was going to the library to study. I stopped sleeping at night. I started having trouble breathing in lectures or in shops. I cried driving to and from university because I was on my own and no one could see. I binged at night alone in the kitchen when everyone else was in bed and crept silently into the garden to vomit into a plastic bag that I threw over the fence into the field. I fantasised about dying in a car crash.

The GP listened, was kind and put me on my first antidepressant that was slowly upped over a few months while I waited for some miracle to happen, to start feeling brighter or better. The GP warned it could be months before it had any effect, but in hindsight I wish she'd also told me I needed to help it along by doing good things for myself. Naively, I thought it would work all on its own.

A few months later, with no real changes other than constant worried looks from my mum and regular blood tests and heart monitoring because of the bulimia, I had six weeks of cognitive behavioural therapy (CBT) with a lady who made me admit some of the bad thoughts that came into my head like 'I'm fat' or 'I'm ugly' or 'I'm useless'. She tried to get me to challenge them, but I can see now I was too low to recognise that they might not have been accurate and I had no desire or energy to take them to task. When she asked over and over, 'Where is the evidence for that thought?', I told her it was in the mirror every day, but apparently that wasn't the right answer. I was too far gone by this point, those thoughts so deeply entrenched in me and the depression so heavy and overwhelming that I couldn't make any progress. I wasn't getting better and that gave me another reason to beat myself up.

By the third or fourth visit to her I had stopped eating and started exercising obsessively. My annual routine of rapidly losing weight for summer had started, which she took as a good sign that I was getting healthier and happier even though it was the opposite. My period wouldn't come and my hair was shedding and thinning as it always did when I didn't eat, but she couldn't see any of that. Wanting to do well at something, I answered her questions as she wanted them answered. She discharged me after the six weeks, patting herself on the back and thinking she had done a great job.

I had an appointment with the GP every few weeks for a check-in with the new medication. Each time, the doctor and my mum asked me if I would take a break from finishing university, but I was in my fourth and final year and had worked incredibly hard and I couldn't walk away. I'd been spending every free moment working on my dissertation and studying for my exams because I was desperate to succeed in one area of my life. I was convinced that if I made it to graduation, the pressure would disappear and I'd naturally start to get better. Looking back, I can't believe I completed that year with my head in the state it was. I struggled through placements, teaching practice, group projects and assignments with a constant poisonous dialogue in my head telling me I was disgusting, everyone hated me and to kill myself. But with an expert mask always glued to my face in public and every minute that I didn't have to be 'on' lying in darkness in bed, I made it.

The funny thing is, I don't think anyone except my mum had a clue what was happening. I was great at pretending everything was fine. I met up with friends as little as I could get away with but just enough that no one would ask questions. The effort of talking and smiling and pretending not to be dying inside floored me with exhaustion. All I was capable of doing was driving to class and coming home to work. I used up any energy I had getting to lectures and having conversations with friends. When I came home I went straight to my room, unable to even give one-word answers to my family. One of the best things Mum did for me then was to say, 'I know it's not ideal, but I'm glad you can come home and be yourself'. Although it wasn't really me, I felt relieved and less guilty knowing I could come home, shut the door and stop pretending for a few hours. I knew she understood how hard I was working during the day to fool everyone.

Despite everything, I completed the course with First-Class Honours and smiled through graduation, hoping I would get better and things would be okay. When I look back at photos from events like my leaving ceremony, formal and graduation, I can see the sadness and exhaustion in my eyes that no one else knew was there. I remember trying so hard at things I'd never had to try at before – getting dressed, walking into a room, smiling for a photo. I was lying to everyone, surrounded on those big occasions by my best friends and family, but I thought I was doing the right thing protecting them from the hurt I was feeling. I was clinging on to life by my very fingertips. But, still, I had hope that everything would start to get better.

I took a teaching job for a year in England thinking that getting away would be a good thing, and for a while it was. I went over with great housemates from university and the distraction of the new house, new country, new job kept me so busy that sometimes I even enjoyed myself and I got some relief from having more privacy and space than I'd ever had before. I loved the anonymity of being away from home. At the weekends my housemates and I, exhausted from teaching all week, would rarely get dressed. Instead we drank and ate from Friday to Sunday night, talking about how drained we were and how there was no way we could teach for the next forty years. We walked to the shop in our pyjamas for chocolate and wine because no one knew us and we finally had a wage coming in every month so we wanted to spend it. This freedom however threw my eating habits into chaos – worse than they'd ever been. I'd always felt I was in control with the bulimia and that if I got my mood stable, being sick would stop, but now it was growing into a totally separate beast.

With no one judging or watching what I was eating, I abused my body with constant bingeing and purging day and night. I'd sometimes be sick up to thirty times a day. I had my own private bathroom for the first time but I could make myself sick anywhere. I could complete a binge and purge cycle in five minutes. I would eat the sweets for the kids out of my treat drawer in the classroom and then be sick in the toilets at school, or stop off at a McDonald's on the way home and eat two burgers with chips without even tasting them before vomiting in a plastic bag and dumping it on the pavement. Then I'd go home and make dinner, which also ended up in the toilet. I remember sneaking to the kitchen in the middle of the night when my friends were fast asleep to raid the cupboards for food and then vomit before climbing back into bed. Once I crept to the kitchen at two in the morning just to go through the bin for half a pizza my housemate had thrown away earlier. I had lost all control and being away from home found it easier to keep up this lifestyle.

When my first year teaching was nearly up and it was time to come home, I thought seriously about taking time off and really trying to tackle the issues in my head. I'd been pushing depression away with an eating disorder but knew it was only a matter of time before it caught up with me again. Then a good school close to home rang and offered me a job – no interview needed. I was even able to pick the class I wanted. It was too good an opportunity to turn down and I kidded myself into believing it was better to be busy and distracted for another year. I told myself I'd sort myself out back home.

Within weeks of my flight landing in Belfast that summer I was back to the same dangerous thoughts I'd had when I left. I'd buried them deep down for so long, ignoring and silencing and distracting myself by replacing any negative thought with a binge and purge. Coming back to my old life meant they raised their ugly heads again, harder and louder than before. It was like they'd slowly gained strength over the year while I'd refused to acknowledge them and now I had no choice but to succumb.

I spent as much time as possible out of the house. I lied to my mum and said I was meeting friends when in reality I drove to a deserted car park and sat alone for hours thinking over the option of killing myself. I rang Lifeline a few times and they set me up with a counsellor for six sessions, but I was so terrified of anyone finding out the true extent of my depression that I couldn't be honest. By the time I'd warmed up and began to talk about things I hadn't let myself remember for years the sessions were over and I was left with upsetting memories and distressing realisations from years before that I then somehow had to deal with on my own. I'd finally started acknowledging some of the worst triggers from my past but just as I became aware of them time was up. No one was there to help me unpack and make sense of the images and memories I had blocked out for years. I half-heartedly attended my GP appointments and changed antidepressants a few times, but I rapidly unravelled over the course of the year. No one knew, even Mum, because I was an expert in hiding it by then. And again I told myself that maybe if I ignored it, it would go away. I began to think that because I'd been to countless doctors and counsellors over the past two years with no improvement I must be unfixable. I imagined the doctors rolling their eyes at me each time I told them I was trying, sick of me for still existing.

One night, after driving around for hours looking for somewhere to sob in frustration without anyone knowing, I drove to a deserted country road to crash the car into an old wall where I knew I'd hurt no one but myself and definitely die on impact. I wanted to make sure I wouldn't end up in a coma in hospital for the next fifty years, making my family come and see me every day. I'd driven past the wall many times in the weeks before, checking it was the right spot. As my foot hovered over the accelerator, my throat started to close over and I had a panic attack. I turned the car off to try and think and then I screamed and cried and made noises I didn't know I was capable of. I punched myself hard in the face over and over until my cheek and eye socket went numb. I slapped my head with such anger and frustration I was sure I would bruise. I clawed at my hair with such force I was certain I was pulling clumps out with my fingers. I bit my hands until they bled and I scrabbed my legs and arms until the skin broke. I repeatedly threw my head against the window to my right until I thought the glass would give way and smash. I opened the car door to vomit everything inside me out onto the quiet country road. I was sick until I was empty. My nose was running, my eyes were streaming, I was choking on my fingers without stopping, continuing to push them down my throat with no success. My knuckles were bloody and covered in vomit and my throat was sore and scraped from my nails. I coughed up clumps of blood. My throat and stomach burned with acid and there was vomit in my hair and over my chin.

I closed the car door and slumped, exhausted, into the chair. The panic was over. I couldn't continue any longer.

I drove home in a daze, numb, wiping my face and mouth and hands with old napkins in the car. I snuck into bed while everyone slept. I had one clear thought on a loop in my mind: if I died, I wouldn't have to suffer through this any longer. That night I was harassed constantly by thoughts of suicide. The options exploded before my eyes like fireworks. It was all I could think of and I struggled to find any reason to stick around.

This same pattern continued every night for a week: drove to the same spot, foot poised over the accelerator and then panic and sobbing and vomit and blood. By then I had a clear picture of when, where and how it was going to happen. It was Wednesday, and I'd decided I would do it on Friday. On the Thursday night, when I snuck back inside hoping everyone was asleep, Mum caught me crying on the edge of my bed, unable to breathe with another panic attack that had come on unexpectedly. She brought me to the out-of-hours GP who sent me to A&E. I was assessed there at two in the morning, told not to be left alone and set up to see a mental health nurse once a week. I was back in work the next morning. Again, my mum and doctor told me to give up school for a while, but I thought I could make it to the summer holidays in three months' time. There were a few close calls but I made it to the end of term without any of my colleagues or friends or family members outside of my mum and dad knowing I was struggling.

With another school year just about completed, I was exhausted and broken and empty and determined not to apply for a job the following year. I promised myself I would take the time to try and get better because I was barely functioning. I had stopped doing anything for pleasure, like reading or watching TV, going to the cinema or out for meals. I stopped going to exercise classes, pulled out of all the social activities I could without raising suspicion and knew that now I needed a break. My weekly meetings with the nurse had mostly become check-ins to see if I had immediate plans to harm myself because I was too exhausted from living a lie that I hadn't the energy to undertake anything meaningful or worthwhile to help myself beyond surviving day to day.

The few tasks and challenges my nurse had set, like meeting a friend or going for a walk outside, hadn't been given enough attention because any energy was spent keeping myself afloat in school, so I made myself promise I would commit to getting better in the year ahead. But when another good job landed in my lap at the end of June and everyone looked at me like I was mad when I admitted I wasn't looking for work, I convinced myself once again that being busy was good for me, that it wouldn't do not to have a focus and a reason to get up every morning. I couldn't deal with the questions people would ask if I refused. How could I explain if asked about work next year that I was taking time off? It would only lead to more questions I couldn't face or answer. The easiest option was to take the job. The shame that would accompany telling people that I was unemployed and the fear of them sussing me out was enough to push me into another school year that I knew deep down I shouldn't have agreed to. Instead of taking the year off as planned, I now had July and August to recharge and get ready to do it all again come September.

A summer spent worrying over my decision meant I started back to school already set up to fail. My mind barked at me again and again that I couldn't do it, that I wasn't able for it and I was going to fall apart in front of everyone. I had nightmares every night of standing in the middle of my classroom having a panic attack in tears while everyone I had ever met stood round me in a circle and watched while I struggled to breathe.

I was an anxious, emotional mess on the inside and just about keeping it together for the sake of everyone else, but I couldn't sustain it. I didn't even make it to Halloween. About six weeks into the school term I cracked and did the unthinkable – something I thought I would never ever do. I quit.

The kids had gone home and their work was laid out ready for the next day, but instead of being at the staff meeting as planned,

I was crying in the classroom, overwhelmed by the thoughts in my head. A teacher came to tell me the meeting had started and caught me in tears in the corner, so I told her I wasn't feeling well and had to go home. I knew then that I couldn't do it anymore. What if next time I was crying the kids found me? I went to the principal and said I was sorry but I was leaving and wouldn't be back the next day. Understandably, he initially thought I'd had a bad day or maybe that I was hormonal. He kept asking if I'd fallen out with another member of staff because nothing leading up to then had indicated I was struggling. I gave him a very brief synopsis of my mental health journey over the last few years to get him to release me. He was visibly horrified – shocked, but thankfully he let me go.

I wasn't able to say goodbye to any of the children I'd already become attached to or any of the staff who had made me feel so welcome. I left my classroom and walked out without any of the resources or work I had painstakingly built up over the weeks and months and years. Like penance for leaving everybody to deal with my inability to continue, it was compensation for whoever had to come in and pick up the pieces.

I'm still not sure if I did the right thing that day. I've often thought about the children I left and the school and job I walked away from. For months I was terrified of bumping into one of the teachers or parents. It haunts me that I left the way I did but I felt I had no other option. I'm an all-or-nothing person and I gave everything I could to the kids in those first six weeks, but I knew that everything I had wouldn't be enough that year. It wasn't fair on them. They weren't getting the teacher they needed and deserved, and I was sure someone else could come in and do a far better job than I was doing for the rest of the year.

It had also got to the point where I was sobbing right from my gut, making strange animal noises on the journey to and from school and having panic attacks twice a day, usually driving home and before bed. I was barely sleeping and my eating was all over the place, lurching from bingeing and purging to starving myself each day. My eyes were dry and the skin around them cracked from crying constantly whenever I could steal a moment alone and roughly wiping them before anyone noticed. I found no happiness or release anywhere or in anything. Every morning I woke up I wished I hadn't and every night when I lay in bed, I prayed and prayed that God or some stroke of luck would let me die in my sleep and I wouldn't have to get up and do another day.

In the days after I left school I felt a slight weight lift from my shoulders and I thought maybe that was the start of it – from then on I would get better, that having made the decision to finally take time out, things would naturally start to improve. The first few days of being off I was active and focused, making plans and researching activities to fill and structure my days. I wanted to make this time off worthwhile and show myself and others that it was the right thing to do because look how fantastic things are now! But of course I was just trying to distract myself from impending doom, which never works, and everything continued to spiral downwards. I didn't care then about structuring my day or trying new activities and soon I was in a place deeper and darker than I ever thought I could go.

I stopped leaving the house for fear of meeting someone I knew and them asking why I was off on a school day. I was frightened of people I didn't know looking at me and thinking how fat and disgusting and ugly I was. I believed I was a hideous monster who would offend people with my face and body. I was terrified of everything and everyone. The suicidal thoughts I had had came back stronger, more often and more intense. I felt overwhelmed by the thoughts in my head and I could speak to nobody. I had no one to turn to and even if I had, I didn't have the words to explain what was happening. My head was so tortured from the constant abuse that I genuinely thought I was losing my mind. Where else can you go when your own head is a dangerous place to be?

I spent all day in bed and in the evenings when my family got home I pretended I was going for a walk with friends or meeting someone for coffee when really I needed to escape before anyone saw the state I was in. Like before, I spent my evenings driving around, parking in dark deserted streets trying to breathe until it was late enough that I could go home and slip into bed without facing anyone. Each day passed and I felt I had absolutely no control over my mind and thoughts. I counted down the days until I would finally crash the car and it would be over.

The thought of dying was the only thing that allowed me peace and quiet for a few moments before the guilt and panic followed and I became afraid again. The negative, bad thoughts I was having became such real physical forces in my head that I honestly couldn't understand how no one else heard or saw them. The thoughts were so aggressive and loud that I couldn't hear anyone speaking to me anymore. I couldn't hear the voices on television and I couldn't have a conversation with anyone because if I tried, I told myself they were thinking I was a failure, that I looked disgusting and everyone would be better off if I died. There was no room in my head to listen and respond to a conversation, so I stopped having them.

After months of waiting I had an appointment with a psychiatric consultant. When she saw the state I was in she immediately assigned me to the Home Care Team as high risk. They came to my house every day and I hated those visits. It was a different nurse every single time, which wasn't good for me. I found it too difficult to speak openly to a stranger. I usually lied – that I was doing fine that day – or said nothing at all. I had the guilt and shame and embarrassment of them coming to my house where my family tiptoed around us pretending not to see. The only room we had to sit in was the living room with glass windows and doors, so speaking openly or getting upset was never an option in case someone walked past.

About a fortnight after the start of these daily visits I agreed to meet my auntie to walk my dog during the day. It took every ounce of strength I had to get dressed and drive to meet her. Not long into our walk I began to cry, which I was constantly doing anyway, although usually only on my own. I began talking gibberish like a mad woman but I could barely hear myself because of the thoughts screaming in my head.

At that moment one of the Home Care Team nurses rang to let me know when she was coming out to see me that day. My auntie took the phone and told her how low I was. I must have seriously freaked her out. The nurse told my auntie I wasn't allowed to drive myself home. She had to take me back and she wasn't to leave me until either my mum got out of work or she got to the house. An hour later the nurse was in my living room with me. She said she could see the pain I was carrying and trying to cover up, and although initially lying to her I finally gave in and told her she was right. I told her I was going out in my car to crash it when she left. She told me I wasn't allowed to drive anymore and took away the keys. I told her I'd take a kitchen knife and ram it hard and deep into my chest over and over until I was dead. She told me she would take away all the knives. I told her I'd hidden one in my room, weeks before, in case of emergencies. The nurse asked what I'd do if she took away every sharp object I could hurt myself with, and without missing a beat I told her I'd swallow every pill I could find or smash a glass and use it to slice up my wrists or take a belt from my dad's wardrobe and loop it over the strong tree I'd picked out in the garden to hang myself from.

I wasn't crying when I told her my plans because I wasn't sad anymore. I wasn't scared either, like I usually was. The exhaustion had floored me and outweighed any nerves I had over dying. It felt like the last and only option to save myself from this torture. Admitting it to the nurse, knowing I was telling the truth, I felt relief and peace and I was proud of myself. It felt good to say it out loud and I felt calmer having finally made a decision. I felt something close to happy for the first time in months.

The nurse made a phone call while I imagined my family's reaction when they got the news I was dead, then the next thing was she told me I had to go stay in the hospital. She told me that if I said no, I had to go anyway and she didn't want that. My mum had left work early to come home to take over from my auntie and I remember her starting to cry when the nurse told her I'd agreed to be admitted.

Mum packed pyjamas and toiletries into a suitcase while I watched her from my bed, and then we were on the road to the hospital. On the way over I think I was in shock – I can't remember the journey through Belfast. What I can remember is getting a call from Lifeline. I had rung a month before and this was them calling me back to offer more counselling sessions. I told the girl on the phone that I didn't need them now because I was on my way to a mental hospital.

I'm not sure if I'm glad the nurse stopped me that day and whether I did the right thing telling her the truth. Part of me that I didn't know still existed must have wanted to be saved and survive. If I ever get through this, in weeks or months or years maybe I'll be glad she didn't leave that day until she knew I was safe.

I can only hope too that some day leaving my job and everything falling apart might turn out to be the right thing and what needed to happen. In better moments I live in hope that this is the start of my recovery and one day I'll wake up and things won't be as bad.

Day 6

Comfort in Him?

There's a new student nurse on the ward today who woke me up with a knock on the door. He isn't even attractive but that doesn't stop me trying to look as normal and sane as possible. I put on a sports bra and brush my hair for the first time in three days.

I can't put what I'd like to on my breakfast tray because he is there handing out tablets and I'm sure he'll immediately think FAT! GREEDY, DISGUSTING FAT PIG! if I take cereal *and* toast. For some reason I think he'd notice that and recoil at the thought of me eating, so I take a tiny spoonful of cereal. I've been stealing biscuits from the unguarded tea tray that sits in the kitchen (most of the people here aren't fit to walk round there on their own, which is why they can leave them out) and have a stash hidden in my suitcase. I can eat those instead.

It's an hour later and I've eaten sixteen biscuits, vomited them up when the coast was clear to the bathroom, had a panic attack over where the hell I am and punched myself in the face until my cheekbones swell up and bruise. I go to ask for a sleeping tablet because this day is too much already and it's not even 10 a.m.

It's the young male nurse at the medication table. I stand, red-eyed and blotchy, with my hair sticking to my forehead from the vomiting, a streaming snotty nose and a few sobs catching my breath every so often while my breathing tries to settle. We make eye contact for the first time and I think what an idiot I am. I'm not even a girl to him. I'm hardly even a person. To him, and to every other nurse and doctor in here, I'm a dramatic crazy loser who has found herself sharing a psych ward with the over sixty-fives who have no teeth and piss themselves. I'm a patient held in a ward so I don't kill myself and that's all I'll be for a long time. Sometimes I forget what I've become.

I don't let Mum visit today because I can't pull myself together and it will only make her feel worse to see me in this state. I have to stay strong as she practically begs and pleads over text to call in for a minute or two. I'm the worst daughter and person in the world but I still don't budge, and a sort of grief that I'm not able to let her in and share some of the shit I'm going through washes over me. I'm jealous of other people and their ability to say what they feel. Maybe if I had had someone I could speak to and confide in, things might not have escalated like they did and this place could have been avoided. But it's the hardest thing in the world to even imagine admitting to anyone close to me that I'm not okay or that things have happened that have made me hate myself and all I want to do is hurt myself beyond repair. I worry what people will think of me – that everyone will flee and leave me if I'm honest, or, worse, I might make them feel sad or fill them with awful thoughts too. I don't want to taint anyone else's life with this. But mostly I worry that if I open up or cry or confess, I'll never be able to stop, literally never stop crying or screaming until I fall apart and can't be put back together again. It feels safer to keep it all tight inside me and say nothing to anyone.

The little nun came to see me again today. She knocked on my door and sat down with such ease and energy for someone who must be at least ninety. I was worried she'd want to pray together again and I cursed myself for my habit of ticking the Catholic box on the admission form. She talked generally for a while and then said, 'You've been having a hard time lately'. I was taken aback for a moment because no one in here asks those questions. And, weirder still, she didn't seem afraid of the answer. Even the nurses beat around the issue and never actually mention anything about depression or suicide or anxiety to me. Yet even with her open, kind face that held no judgement, I didn't say anything honest or admit to anything, as always. I don't know why I couldn't, because she wanted me to share with her and I wanted to, but I couldn't bring myself to tell the truth. I just nodded and said, 'A little'. She told me how lots of people find comfort in God and prayer when they go through difficult times and I agreed with her only because I didn't want to make it awkward. I thought for a second about telling her that I feel comfort when she's here sitting opposite me, but I was too shy to speak. She left me the bulletin from the Mass again, which I wasn't sure what to do with because you aren't allowed to throw holy things in the bin, are you? She gave me a soft pat on the shoulder and her smell lingered again, like it did before, reminding me of my granny for hours after.

After a mostly sleepy day (thanks to a sedative), I am ashamedly excited with the drama happening in the corridor. From what I can gather Ellen is kicking off because no one went to the shop to get her cigs and full-fat Coke (she isn't allowed to leave the ward except to go to the smoking area a few times a day when a nurse is free). The nurses keep telling her it's because she hasn't any money for the shop but she's convinced the social worker said she'd left some for her in the office. I'm sure the nurses aren't lying but I feel for the scary little woman. She is angry and shouting now and for a second I wish I smoked so I could give her one to calm her down – although actually she seems to have forgotten about the smokes and is shouting and stamping about something else now. This is the most noise and action this ward has seen all week.

I'm suddenly worried the nurses are laughing at Ellen behind her back. Like in school when the teachers talk about a kid or a parent having a tantrum or a strop and everyone laughs in the staffroom. I'm sure that happens in the nurses' room too. Are they making notes right now to share about Ellen later over their tea? What have they said about me? Am I crazy and scary like

Ellen but don't realise it? She doesn't even know I exist but I want to protect her. She's vulnerable and alone out in the corridor ranting and raving like a child who's overtired. She never has any visitors. Who brings her snacks and does her washing?

Later, around midnight, I sneak from my room to the bathroom and see Ellen fast asleep, wrapped in a blanket, on the sofa by the door opposite the nurses' station in protest.

Day 7

Rock Bottom

A theme is emerging because just like yesterday and the day before, today is not a good day. I'm worried because I can't remember the last good one.

It started when no one woke me for breakfast. The sounds of voices and cutlery woke me anyway and as I lay waiting for a nurse to call me like they always do, I realised no one was coming.

My anxiety skyrocketed. I imagined everyone in the dining room whispering and talking about me, laughing at me alone in my room, which is ridiculous because none of the old people in here know their own names never mind mine. Maybe the nurses think I'm fat enough without having more food? Maybe they're trying to make me skinnier and less disgusting by missing breakfast? Maybe they've forgotten I'm here at all?

Insecure enough to need to know, I shuffled round the corner to an obligatory 'Morning' from one of the male nurses who didn't look up from the chart he was studying. The rest didn't acknowledge me at all – oh, God, what have I done? I think back over the last week for clues as to how I've messed up. They're sick of me being here, I decide. They think there's nothing wrong with me. They think I'm taking up the bed of someone who is really sick and needs to be here. Why am I not better yet so I can go home?

I'm late. The tea and toast is already gone, so I pour myself some Bran Flakes before realising they've already taken the milk away. There's no way I'm asking for milk and making a fuss or drawing attention to myself, so I leave the bowl and go back to my room empty-handed with my eyes on the floor to avoid anyone seeing I'm crying.

Soon after, without realising I'm doing it, I google on my phone how to kill yourself in a hospital ward. In seconds hundreds of links flood the small screen. I tell myself I'm just looking out of curiosity. Most of the findings are case studies looking into the failings of mental health hospitals in stopping patients from suicide and I scan them looking for details on how the patients were found dead in their rooms. I find forums from ex-patients and ex-cons discussing stories they heard of how people died in their jail cells and hospital rooms.

Research over, I look around the room and decide that jumping out the window is impossible – although we are on the top floor, which would have been perfect. The windows are big and thick and heavy and can only be opened an inch or two from the bottom, which is covered in meshed metal. I wonder if the windows are only impenetrable because someone tried what I was thinking. Overdosing is out of the question: the nurses hand you each tablet and watch you swallow them before locking the medicine cupboards. I sneak from my room and check the handle on the cleaning cupboard round the corner but the door is locked, which means downing bleach and whatever else I'd have found in there is a no go too. My razor to shave my legs (did I actually think I would bother doing that in here?) was taken off me when I first checked-in, we're given weird blunt butter knives like you get in the airport with our meals and we aren't allowed glass for drinks. Hanging myself is the only option, I surmise. I scan the room and pull lightly on the flimsy curtains that give immediately. There is nothing to hang from in my cell – even the short cord on the light bulb is nothing more than a string.

I put my head down and take the few steps from my room into the shared bathroom, which is past the nurses' station but they're sorting out medication with the patients in the dining room and won't be there. I lock the door behind me and look around. I move the disabled showering chair under the shower rail's strongest point, where it's held by an extra support from the ceiling. I stand on the chair and pull hard with both hands on the shower rail. It doesn't move at all. Satisfied it will take my weight, I run back to my room, the corridor still empty with breakfast wrapping up. I unplug my straighteners and wind the strong, thick cord around them.

There follows twenty minutes of pacing up and down (out of view of the tiny window in my door and therefore the nurses), crying silently, sobbing, imagining my friends' and family's faces if I carry out my plan. Years ago a therapist told me to do that when I feel like this, but it isn't enough to put me off the idea today. I don't care about my friends and family right now. I think about the past week in hospital and how nothing has changed – in fact, things are worse. No one has tried to help me or offer any solutions or a plan out of this. When I can't sleep, I'm given more sleeping pills. When I can't sit still with anxiety or am in a constant cycle of panic attacks, I'm given sedatives. Why does no one ask why I can't sleep, why I'm so anxious, why I'm panicking? I came here to get help and support and get better but I'm consumed instead with pure pain in every inch of my body – screaming in my head and the pounding of my heart and lungs at what feels like ten times the normal rate. The only thing stopping me now is me. I'm scared but I don't know what else to do.

The third or fourth time I put my hand on the door to head to the bathroom with the straighteners tucked into my waistband and hidden below my baggy jumper, a nurse walks past. I don't know her name but I shout a pathetic 'Hey!' to her as she walks past. I didn't mean to – it was an automatic reaction. In a stammered few words I tell her, 'The shower rail can hold my weight'. She stares at me then says, 'What will you use?' I lift up my jumper and take out my straighteners, which she takes from me. I'm embarrassed, annoyed at myself, also relieved? Maybe. She comes into my room and takes the hairdryer and fan – anything with a cord. She asks if my razors were already taken from me. I stand by while she gathers everything she can from my room, feeling like a fucking idiot and wanting to throw myself off a bridge. I can't even do this right. I'm stupid and shit at everything. Completely useless.

Leaving with my things, she thanks me for telling her and I'm taken aback for a second by the look on her face. I didn't expect to see worry in her expression. I thought this would be second nature to the nurses here – that they see it every day and are immune to it, but her face is sad. She tells me not to move and she'll be back soon. I say okay but I can't look at her I'm that embarrassed. She didn't need to tell me not to move because I'm stuck, still standing by the door where I called to her from.

I'm sure she's telling everyone about me now. They'll say that if I really meant it, I'd have done it and how I must be looking for attention. Maybe they're right. Maybe I was looking for attention, waiting for someone to help me. Surely I wouldn't be so undecided if I really wanted it to happen. Something took over when I called out to Katya (she told me her name) that didn't want to loop those straighteners round the bar in the bathroom. My stomach is contracting thinking of the nurses talking and whispering about me and hating me, and I sit on the bed pleading and begging for it all to be over.

A few hours later I wake disorientated with heavy eyes after the diazepam Katya gave me earlier to take the edge off. She said it would help me get through this bad day but it has wiped me out. I stumble to the bathroom and see that it has changed. The shower rail has been taken down from the wall and removed, and the chair I had stood on earlier is gone too. Disgracefully ashamed and embarrassed, I keep my head down until I get back to my room. Everyone is staring at me even though no one is about.

When I'm back in my room trying to process the change in the bathroom that occurred while I was out of it, I realise I'm relieved. I can relax now that the temptation and the option has been taken away from me. Without the rail I can stop obsessing over the quality of my blanket or bed sheet as a noose and for the first time I feel safe here. There is nothing more I can do to harm myself tonight. I fall asleep exhausted but easier than I have in weeks.

Day 8

The Binge Cycle

After breakfast, and still feeling the effects of yesterday's wobble, I lose control and binge on everything I can find in my room: four packets of crisps, a sandwich from the shop, a family-sized bar of chocolate, half a pack of grapes and an apple, two bags of sugar-free gummy bears – everything Mum brings when she visits – and then the hospital biscuits I've been sneaking from the kitchen and stockpiling for this scenario. When that's all gone, I even swallow a sachet of hot chocolate powder, gagging but determined to get it down. It's taken less than ten minutes. I stuff the wrappers inside a ball of tissues and put it under my jumper to dispose of in the corridor bin on my way to the bathroom.

I kneel in front of the toilet seat and hold it up, give the rim a wipe with toilet roll and push up my sleeves. Thankfully I cut my nails last night or my throat would be in bits after this. I tie my hair back in a ponytail and push two fingers down my throat as far as they can go, past my tonsils, until the familiar gag kicks in, my stomach contracts and I bring up the food not yet digested by my stomach. I vomit quietly and close to the bowl to not make a sound as the slop hits the inside. I'm sick twelve or thirteen times until there is nothing left. There's relief and I'm reset for the day. At least this is something I can do that I'm good at. I never fail at this. My face is red and blotchy, splashed with vomit and stained with tears. My right hand is disgusting, cut and bloody from my back teeth but I'm sufficiently punished. My head is briefly quiet.

I try to cool my face with water and gargle until I can get to my room to brush my teeth. I unlock the door and think that someone will say something – maybe they heard or saw me rush to the bathroom and now see me emerging looking a guilty mess. But none of the nurses even look up when I shuffle past. That's what I want but weirdly, I'm disappointed. I realise that I want to get caught, that despite everything I'm doing to myself I still want help. I don't want to be trapped in this exhausting cycle of bingeing and purging but I don't know how to stop. I've tried so many times before and promised myself that each time is the last time, but it's like an addiction. I lose control and find moments of comfort in food before the guilt and disgust panics me into such a frenzy that half the time I've sicked up everything inside me without even realising it's started. It's like my body is on autopilot and I'm just a passenger along for the ride.

I know the ridiculous bingeing-purging-starving routine I put my body through multiple times a day doesn't help my energy levels or fluctuating weight but I'm helpless and overwhelmed and it quiets my head because it physically drains me until I need to sleep. I'm screaming and howling and crying and thrashing inside before a binge but I'm master of the poker face and to everyone else I'm calm and collected and coping. No one ever knows about the tears and the sickness and that I'm already planning for the next time.

Where the beginning of the depression is vague and messy and impossible to pin down, I remember the exact moment the bulimia started. I was nearly 18 and studying for my A-levels. I had come home from school to an empty house and deciding if I should have dinner or skip it to lose weight for the weekend. I became overwhelmed then with such hatred for my body and felt like no matter how little I ate or how much I exercised it would never be enough to make me like myself. To swallow down the feelings that were beginning to bubble up inside me I binged on everything I could get away with which wasn't uncommon. But this time when it was over I felt so disgusted with myself that I knew I needed something more immediate than restricting my food and over-exercising for the next few days to counteract what I'd just done.

Like a lightbulb moment I remembered from Home-Economics class that there were people who made themselves sick when they ate too much. This seemed like the answer to all my problems so I took myself off to the bathroom, rolled up my sleeves and stared at the toilet bowl. I had a clear thought in my head that this was a bad idea. I knew that I shouldn't do this, I shouldn't start this, even just this one time. I could tell that this was a darker and different level of abuse against my body I was entering into and I knew that this could lead me down an even trickier path. But the lure of finding a way to quickly erase everything I had eaten was too strong and so I did it anyway.

I have regretted that moment so many times over the years. If I'd listened to myself and stepped away from the bathroom I wouldn't still be struggling with this powerful addiction six years later that I can't get in control of. What makes it even worse is that when I couldn't quite master it that first time, instead of giving up, I decided to persevere time and time again until I became able to do what I wanted and rid myself of the binge. That made the binges far more regular when I felt like I could 'justify' them by being sick after. Every time I go to be sick I think back to that first time and how different things could have been.

Ugh! I make it back to my room and am brushing my teeth at the sink when a new student nurse knocks on my door and lets herself in to sit on my bed. She watches, a smile on her skinny face, while I spit and then introduces herself. When you despise yourself, your appearance, everything you say and do, it's not helpful if a nineteen-year-old perky blonde, skinny student nurse tells you to try meditating or colouring in to get better. I tell her I'll give them a try and she skips out of the room pleased with herself.

Once nurse Barbie left, it took superhuman strength to make my bed. Drained from emptying my guts and having to fill a minute of small talk, it feels like each of my limbs is solid lead and my brain is pure mush. It takes half an hour to lift the blanket and lay it back down again. I spend most of that time staring at the bed, willing myself to move and get started. It feels like I'm trying to move a mountain and I wonder whether it's my head or my body making it difficult. I'm exhausted afterwards and need to get back into bed when I'm finished, undoing the good work. How weird that I can't even lift a duvet without it taking everything out of me. My arms and legs feel weighted and I struggle to move them. I'd be worried there's something wrong with them but I'm too tired to care. I sleep for a few hours and don't even sit up when my mum comes for the afternoon visit. I let her brush the floor and wipe around the sink and from the bed watch her leave fresh pants, my eyes only half-open. She leaves the curtains half-closed for me and I think how disappointed she must be in me. I'm a mess. No one wants a daughter like this.

I'm on the way to the bathroom for my weekly shower when I spot someone I know and freeze. There's a group of about four or five doctors standing outside the nurses' station and I instantly recognize the side profile of one of them. He is a friend of a friend but I've met him a few times before; I've even been on a night out with him not so long ago. I knew he was a doctor but the thought never crossed my mind that he would be here. He hasn't spotted me so I turn and run back into my room. I feel panic start to rise up inside me and I can feel myself getting hotter. What if he already knows I'm here? I'm sure my name is on a whiteboard in the nurses' station. And I don't exactly blend in with the rest of the OAPs. But, I try to reason with myself, even if he does know I'm here, he can't tell anyone surely? I know there's a patient-doctor confidentiality thing, but do they actually stick to that? I'm hiding in the corner of my room again when one of the nurses puts her head round my door to tell me dinner is ready. I blurt out to her that I know one of doctors and I don't want him to know anything about me being here. She seems surprised but then says that she'll pass the message on that he's not to sit in on any of the meetings the doctors and nurses have about me. I feel so relieved that my head goes light, but when she leaves and I'm replaying the conversation in my head something clse is annoying me now. I didn't know the doctors and nurses came together to have meetings about us. I feel uncomfortable imagining the staff all sitting round a big table talking about me. What could they be saying? I spend the majority of the days here sitting alone in my room; I've barely said two words to anyone so none of them would know how I'm doing. And I haven't heard of any sort of treatment that's been decided, so what else do they talk about in these meetings? I start to feel like I'm being watched, so on my way round to dinner I don't make eye contact with anyone.

Day 9

Rocky Visits

My ward is the top floor of four. I've been to the first floor before – it's a sort of mental health A&E at night and I was sent there one evening about a year ago by an out-of-hours doctor I spoke to on the phone. I was there until two-ish in the morning (I remember because I was working the next day) but all they said was to keep taking my meds.

The second floor is for males under sixty-five. When I was admitted here (the last time I was outside) we took the stairs and passed the big glass doors of the male ward. It was noisy and there were bodies everywhere.

The next floor up is the female under sixty-five ward and I thanked God I wasn't going there because a group of nineteen or twenty-year-old girls, four of them, stared at me when I passed. I felt like I was walking past the cliques in school.

Then, finally, there's the fourth floor with the old people and me.

An OT from the downstairs female ward visited this morning to invite me to join some of the activities they have down there. They must have heard I was up here on my own and thought I was struggling, which I am but not because of that. Apparently there's a few girls my age who do activities together, like nails and hair and make-up. I can't imagine anything worse than having to speak to anyone or have a beauty session with them, especially anyone born in the same decade. I imagine it: me in the middle of four or five pretty, skinny girls more streetwise and cooler than me who don't want to waste their make-up on a face like mine. I lie and tell her I'll think about it. For the first time I'm grateful to be surrounded by geriatrics who are yet to realise I exist.

Later, just as I'd been thinking I hadn't had any air for over a week, one of the nurses told me I'd been granted an accompanied short pass within hospital grounds. That meant I could leave the ward for the first time with a family member or nurse for up to twenty minutes, but had to stay on hospital grounds. She didn't give a reason – I wondered if it's like jail where you get rewarded for good behaviour, but then I remembered the bathroom incident, so it couldn't be that. Do they think I'm getting better? I don't know what they've seen to make them think I'm improving, but of course I do my crying and panicking and vomiting and hitting when no one can see.

It'll be the first time I've seen anything outside my bedroom, the bathroom and the canteen in over a week and my head's light at the thought of the extra air and space I'll be exposed to. I'm not sure I actually want to go outside but I have to now I'm allowed. I text my mum and ask her to bring Rocky, my six-month-old golden retriever, to the doors of the ward. Stupidly I'm nervous to go outside, even though all I can do is hover about the doorway that leads to the car park.

I was 100 per cent sure this would do me so much good. Yes, I didn't like the thought of going outside, but I knew I would be happier for the short time Rocky was here and I hoped the feeling would linger a while. I was hoping for once to feel a smile on my face (I couldn't remember the last time) and experience comfort. I needed to get rid of the huge, heavy, overbearing guilt that constantly pressed down on my chest for leaving him and giving the responsibility of him over to my mum and dad when I was moved here.

I was also desperate to see him because I was terrified he'd forgotten me and wouldn't love me anymore. Because he's still a baby I felt I was missing him grow and worried he'd have changed from a puppy into a dog in the last nine days.

Waiting for Mum to drive over I thought about how, although I had got Rocky just four months ago to help get me out of the house, be active, face people and have a purpose and a reason to get out of bed each day, he had instead become a good way of hiding in public. Everyone flocked to him and cooed over him and I hardly got a second glance – exactly how I wanted it. He helped make up for my shortcomings; he distracted people from looking at me and judging me and thinking how ugly and fat I am.

In the past few months, when I came close to hurting myself, it helped to think of him and how young he is and how I couldn't leave him.

Well, once again I got it wrong. Instead of feeling elated, buoyed and relieved after seeing him, I'm heartbroken. I can feel it now as I scribble in this notebook, a raw and grief-like ache when I saw him and realised he is still perfect. He is happy and healthy and being spoilt completely rotten. My mum and dad love him even more now. They've clearly put the energy they used to put into looking after me into looking after him.

He was happy to see me and recognised me but he was so full of energy and enthusiasm and excited to be in a new place that he would have reacted the same with anybody. In fact, when one of the scary women from the female ward came to the doors in her pyjamas for a smoke, he was as happy to see her as he was to see me. I let Mum and Dad talk away to her about Rocky while I sat on the step feeling more alone than ever. I know now that he doesn't really need me. Him relying on me was a safety net I called on to talk myself out of dying but now it's gone. He's fine without me. He's happy. He can't bring me the relief or joy or hope or strength I desperately needed to feel, and so the dark, dark thoughts are back louder and stronger than I ever remember them. Like the final nail in the coffin, now I know that dying is the only option.

Day 10

The Doctor's Schedule

I'm like a broken record but today is another bad day. When will it end? I wish I'd something different or more exciting to say instead of repeating the same old thing, but this is the reality. I'm still reeling from the night before when I was panicked and sobbing and couldn't sleep. I asked for a sedative in the middle of the night while the nurses stared at me from their station. They seemed to sigh and roll their eyes at the state I was in. I felt it was my fault, that the nurses hated me for annoying them. I cried in my bed as quietly as I could until I must have fallen asleep. But the pain and the panic is still overwhelming this morning, like a pounding headache in both temples. I know they're there and they frighten me but there's nothing I can do to take them away. It feels like a day where I need to be careful and just get through until it's time for bed again.

I have no energy or willpower to do anything today. I swallow a piece of toast without tasting it and stare out my window, watching people on the street below going about their business. I try fleetingly to give myself a shake and see if I can rid the blackness of today, but the day stretches painfully out ahead and it's no use, it's a goner. I don't even leave back my breakfast tray and instead close the curtains, turn off the light and get back into bed. In sleep I'm not plagued by the thoughts. I can escape for a few hours and get closer to tomorrow, hoping it will be better. I'm sorry to anyone who comes near me today.

The next thing I know my door opens, the light switches on and I'm told the doctor has called me. It doesn't matter how bad you are or how awful your mood is, we work on the doctor's schedule.

I drag myself out of bed to the interviewing room but I have nothing left for manners or gratefulness or thankfulness for being here, and it shows. I answer the exact same questions he asked the first time but I don't bother to look at him or elaborate when he asks me to. I stare at the floor and give single-word monotone answers. I know how rude I'm coming across but I can't do anything more than this right now. 'How are you doing?' What a stupid question. I caught a glimpse of my reflection in the window on the way here. One look at me and he should know I'm struggling to keep it together. My eyes are swollen and puffy, my skin is covered in red blotches brought on by stress and I'm still in my pyjamas. Unsurprisingly, it's clear he hasn't called me in to offer help or solutions, which is the only reason I got out of bed, so I give up answering and shrug off the last of his questions. We both know I'm beyond engaging with him and anything he asks. Eventually, after a long pause when I can feel him staring at me, he says, 'You seem angry today', and then all the anger I had towards him and how completely useless he's been since I got here dissipates and instead I want to die immediately, on the spot. I'm embarrassed and hate every inch of myself more than I thought possible. He thinks I'm a rude, horrible little bitch, which I am, and he'll probably kick me out of here.

I don't mean it. I can't help it. I'm sorry. I'm really, really sorry.

But while I'm repenting in my head and thinking how I can answer his questions properly, he says something about how important it is to 'work *with* the medication'. I catch my breath, feeling like the air has been pushed out of me. Behind my eyes my brain erupts and it takes everything in me not to open my mouth and scream like a banshee in his face (if only I had the energy). He's blaming me for not trying hard enough. Sweet Lord, help me. Is this real life? Does he understand what depression is? Does he know what it does? Surely he's had to read a book on it at the very least. Does he think I'm doing this on purpose? I'm trying as hard as I possibly can. How can he think I choose to live this way? Why would anyone, ever, do this to themselves? I'm doing absolutely everything I can to stay alive despite every second of every day being torturous. How does he think I should behave? What does he think I should be doing? I don't want to be here, but I am, for what feels like everyone else's sake.

He knows looking at the mess I am today that I don't have the energy or motivation to brush my teeth, get dressed or even sit up straight, but he chatters on regardless, talking at me. I zone back in for a second when he suggests breathing (hadn't thought of that), sitting in the communal area for 'socialisation', and 'chit-chat' with the staff. I don't mean to be rude but is he not supposed to be a specialist of some sort to be the lead doctor in here? Is it any wonder opening up about your mental health has such stigma attached to it when the 'treatments' being recommended are to 'breathe from your gut'? Is it any wonder there's a bloody mental health pandemic? How can a seriously sick person ever recover with this 'care'?

I'm back in the room, still staring at the floor trying to process what this useless man has proffered. He's stopped talking now, I notice with relief. I chance a glance up at him to see if he's waiting for a response and he looks to be making a move to leave. Oh, my! This is really it! This is the insight I've been waiting patiently for in my little cell for over a week. I can't believe he gets paid for this. What a smug, rich idiot! I thought I was bad, but here we have an even bigger fraud and more useless individual.

That's it, I decide. I need to check out of this narrative to protect myself and let anything else he's going to say go completely over my head. I close my ears to him. I won't hear another word. I vacate the conversation for fear it will make me angrier and more hurt and I can't cope with any more emotion in my head right now. I know later, alone in my room, I'll play through this conversation a thousand times, each time feeling worse than the last, so I need to block out as much as possible to minimise the damage.

It crosses my mind briefly, in one quick flash, that he probably didn't mean to upset or hurt me, but then, actually, that's not good enough because he has and he should know better. A friend is training to be a doctor. It's constant exams, placements, study. They must cover the basics – how to speak to patients 101. How does he not know how harmful his words are? I thought doctors would understand, or at least be more careful. I trusted him. I assumed he could and would make me better but it's clear that he can't and won't.

Shit! Maybe it's me. Maybe there's nothing that can be done. Maybe I'm just not meant to get better. Is that what he's trying to tell me?

I'm now sure from this painful conversation of feeling two inches tall and being blamed for not trying hard enough to recover, that what I must do is crystal clear. This life, every day, is too tough for me. I'm too weak to handle it and deal with it the way everyone else outside the hospital ward can. Everything is difficult. I struggle to open my eyes fully, walk in a straight line or string a sentence together with the chaos in my head. I can't keep living like this. I'm a terrible person. I'm a burden on everyone because I can't get myself better. I suck the life out of all I come in contact with – they know it and they hate me for it. It's better for everyone if I'm gone. How can I make that happen?

Back in my room I try to distract myself because I'm too exhausted for another panic attack. I open the book Mum packed for me a week and a half ago. I used to love reading and got through a book a day during the summer holidays but it's been months – years actually, since I've had the motivation or energy to read or the ability to concentrate and sit patiently for more than a line and take any of the words in.

I struggle through a page or two, rereading the lines repeatedly and doing my best to drag my thoughts away from the demons in my head to focus on the descriptions and characters when it becomes clear that the husband in the book is depressed and his wife doesn't know what to do. I wonder if Mum sent this book by accident or on purpose. I give up at Page 4.

Day 11

How Did I Get Here?

I'm allowed to go further than the car park today – I still have to stay on hospital grounds and be away for no more than half an hour or they'll send a search party – and I let my friend come for the occasion. Desperate for a change of scene we walk through the hospital, but the only places to go are either the bright busy canteen packed wall-to-wall with visitors or the little empty chapel. The thought of people staring at me in my pyjamas under the fluorescent lights nearly makes me wish for the ward, so we opt for the empty chapel instead. We sit in silence for a few moments and I think of the little nun who visited and how calm I'd felt the times she was with me. With the candles and the quiet and the incense I have the same feeling again. It's peaceful – even my thoughts know this is a moment to be still and quiet. Maybe this is the feeling the doctor meant all those years ago when he told me to find religion.

I try to hold on to that sense of peace but as I wave goodbye to my friend at the door of the ward and meet the nurse to walk back inside, I feel the tightness and the noise and the stress return. By the time I'm back in my room the feeling has evaporated.

I'm exhausted from my short trip out. I tried not to put on too much of an act with my friend but it's hard not to – I've had a permanent mask up for years and it's easier to keep up the farce than be myself. I made sure she came when my morning meds (and the previous night's) had worn off because I think she was nervous enough meeting me here never mind seeing me post-tablets when my speech is slurred, I'm walking into walls and my eyes don't fully open.

She asked me the million-dollar question that every doctor, nurse, psychiatrist, psychologist, psychotherapist, counsellor and a few brave family members and friends have: why? What is it? What's happened to make you like this? Why can't you get out of it?

So far no one has been satisfied by the answer (if I've attempted to give them one) and I couldn't give her one either. But, for my own sake, I'm going to try my best to organise the situations and events that have led me here. Maybe a miracle will happen and I can make some sense of it all when it's laid out in black and white before me. I've never done this. I always shut down any memories before I get this far, so here we go.

When I was very little – far too little when I think of the kids in my classroom – I was aware of what seemed like a constant dialogue and obsession surrounding weight, food, body image, FAT. My mum and her friends and my aunties were always on one diet then another; joining then re-joining different groups that promised to make them healthy and happy and skinny. Conversations between them always seemed to be about being good or bad with food, their appearance and if people had lost or gained weight. I grew up surrounded by this and because of it had a clear understanding that fat equals bad and skinny equals good. Nothing else about a person mattered. The adults around me constantly commented on people's size on TV and in magazines – even the appearance and weight of strangers in the street. I have vivid memories from age seven of feeling embarrassed and ashamed of my body compared to the boys and other girls in my class. I believed I was fat and therefore ugly, worthless and a lesser human being than anyone around me. I remember being given a treat by teachers – a sweet or chocolate bar – and thinking that everyone's eyes were on me while I ate, judging me and thinking I was disgusting and that I should say no to 'bad' foods because I was big enough already (I wasn't).

I remember dreading swimming lessons with school at the age of eight. Of having a lump in the pit of my stomach every week leading up to it. I was convinced everyone was staring at my huge body. I spent the entire time sucking in my stomach until my ribs protruded. I once remember the swimming instructors calling me over about a rash I'd developed all over my body. They didn't know what it was but it was my reaction to stress and panic. I get the same red blotches now, nearly two decades later.

I overcompensated for feeling so awful and insecure by always being the funny, loud one in primary school; knowing somehow that I needed to be the funniest or the nicest or most confident to make up for what I believed I lacked physically. I look at my childhood pictures now and see that I was perfect. I wasn't fat. I was a slim, normal child with cute chubby cheeks.

I remember innocent comments from family members of 'she loves her food' and 'she'd eat you if you aren't careful!' that I still feel the sting of now. One time my auntie complained about her sons not eating their dinner and I remember Mum looking at me and laughing, replying that 'at least I'll never have that problem with her!'.

She didn't mean any of it the way I took it. She didn't know I'd already developed a huge insecurity and obsession over my tiny child body – and she probably wasn't even aware of what she was saying. If she knew the effect of her words, she'd be devastated.

The thing is, I'm sure those few comments were surrounded by so many other comments of love and praise but it's only the few that I took negatively that have stuck. I was already hyper-aware of my body and food, so the same comments to another child probably wouldn't have registered. Yet when I'm feeling bitter and wanting someone to blame I think, they should have known better. How did they not notice my face when they said those things? Maybe that was when I first learnt to cover up my feelings.

Another memory that makes me shudder is of my brother standing on a half-broken skateboard owned by the neighbours and it breaking. I secretly cried in my room when I heard the neighbour telling his friends what happened. I thought he was calling my brother fat and in my eyes that was the worst thing you could ever say about a person. I was paranoid that everyone was calling my family fat behind our backs, and I was embarrassed by every part of me – upset that I existed at all. When I looked in the mirror, before my eyes, my stomach protruded, my face blew up like a balloon and my legs thickened like tree trunks until a monster stared back at me. I was convinced that was how I looked and certain that's what everyone else saw too.

Around that time I imagined myself, every night before bed, waking up in a magic bubble that no one could see me in. I could go about my life doing whatever I pleased without anyone having to look at me.

This obsession with my body and warped image I had of myself back then quickly grew into an intense shame and hatred that at that young age I didn't know how to process or express. I thought it was how everyone felt and didn't realise it wasn't the norm.

I tried to mask my pain and find other ways to feel good but every time I achieved something it was never enough. I could never get the happiness or fulfilment I was desperate for. I worked hard in primary school but when I started secondary school it reached a new level. Every single day and night I did more than was expected of me. I spent nights rewriting my notes from school to make them neater and redid homework to make it better, spending hours making my school books look perfect, trying to make up for how ugly I felt.

I threw myself into clubs and extracurriculars to see if those could make me feel better and keep me busy and out of my head. I hoped that if I excelled in other areas, no one would notice how fat and ugly I was on the outside or how sad and anxious I was on the inside. I was desperate to be known as anything other than fat. I had armfuls of hobbies to compensate for my appearance, but I never went near sports clubs despite being desperate to play Gaelic and soccer and netball because I was too scared people would laugh at me for being overweight and unfit. I thought I'd be a liability on a team and wouldn't be the very best at it, so I stayed away.

In my final year of school, when I knew I'd get all As from working solidly, was involved in every extracurricular I could be, was exhausted making sure I was everyone's friend and, the most exhausting of all, pretending I was happy, I still didn't feel good and so began to make myself sick. I felt alone and couldn't process my feelings and my thoughts. Trying to comfort and distract myself, I binged on everything in the cupboards that wouldn't be noticed missing and when the panic and disgust set in I fixed it by teaching myself to vomit it all back up in the bathroom. Being on study leave and home alone, this happened Monday to Friday. Sometimes I planned the binge – went to the shop and bought the foods I didn't usually allow myself: bread, chocolate, buns. Sometimes I visited two or three shops, one after the other to buy my supplies. I was too embarrassed to bring it all to one cashier because I thought they'd judge me and find me disgusting for all the 'bad' foods I was buying. At home I ate everything in a few minutes, not tasting any of it. When it was gone, I immediately got rid of it in the bathroom. I learnt the toilets in the house that did a better job of flushing it away and hid the wrappers in a bag in my room that I walked round to the nearest public bin. My weight fluctuated but I hid in baggy clothes so no one noticed. I lost four or five pounds in a week by spending five days having a bowl of lettuce for lunch, vomiting it up, another for dinner, followed by a run and two gym classes back to back. But by the end of the week I was starving, obsessed with the foods I couldn't have, and binged on a loaf of bread, a tub of ice cream, a twelve pack of crisps, a four pack of chocolate bars and three yogurts in under fifteen minutes, then vomited for half an hour until my stomach was empty and my throat raw and bleeding.

Another factor that probably fuelled the viciousness of my illness is that, unfortunately, I've never been able to open up to anyone in my immediate or extended family. We are not a group who speak openly about our feelings or who share easily. I blame a lot of this, again, on early experiences that I hate thinking about, but here we go.

One Friday – I was around seven or eight, sadly the same time I started to hate my body – I remember having the best day in school. I still remember everything about it. For context, in the week leading up to this Friday, my brother and I had been grounded to our rooms for the first time ever and were only allowed downstairs to eat our dinner. At the time we thought we'd done something wrong but we weren't sure what. We thought Mum and Dad were cross at us and we had been really bad. Now I know that we just needed to be out of the way.

But back to Friday in school – this was a good day. The sun was shining, my best friend's birthday party was that weekend and I had full marks on my spelling test. I remember thinking Mum and Dad would be so happy about my test they would forgive me and my brother and forget whatever we'd done to be grounded and it would be over. Obviously I had no way of knowing, but still I remember skipping to the car that afternoon having this feeling in the pit of my stomach that the day had been too good somehow and something bad would have to balance it out. Then the tummy ache started, which meant something awful was definitely about to happen.

My first clue that something was up that day should have been my granny and granda squeezed into the car with Mum to pick us up from school. That had never happened before, but I thought it was an added surprise to my great day. But still my tummy was hurting. Mum was being extra nice to us on the drive home and when we got back to the house my uncle was there too. There was a weird mood inside and I remember going straight to the bathroom because my tummy was getting worse and I thought I needed the toilet. Then my brother and I were sat down by Mum and told that Dad wasn't living with us anymore because they'd had a big fight and he'd moved out.

She told us that Dad had been late home the night before and his dinner was cold by the time he got it. It had made Mum cross and that's why he was going to live in my other granny's house for a while. Firstly, I thought it was a silly reason to have such a big fight because why couldn't they put the dinner in the microwave? Then I realised that of course Mum was lying and actually they were fighting about me and my brother because we'd been bold (I still couldn't think of anything naughty we'd done but that didn't matter) and so really it was my fault that Dad had to leave.

My uncle took us to McDonald's for a treat and I remember my tiny little head in overdrive thinking how awful I was and how cross and sad I'd made everyone, and how I was such a bad person I was probably going to hell. I had to be extra good and extra nice and maybe I could make up for all the bad things I'd done.

When he was gone my dad sent me and my brother letters that the postman delivered. I imagined him sitting alone at the table in my granny's house, sad and far away. I wanted to talk to him and say how sorry I was and promise to be good and never bad again if he came back to live with us, but I could barely say two words to him when he phoned. I felt torn in ways I didn't understand at that age. I missed him but I knew my mum and family on that side were angry at him. I thought it was because he had moved far away. I was meant to go on day trips with him and my brother, but I was always confused and emotional and I couldn't even look at him when he came to pick us up. I wouldn't let him hug or kiss me and instead hid behind Mum and he left with only my brother for their day out.

I can still see his face perfectly as he stood at the car; his heart breaking when I couldn't talk or look at him even though I wanted to more than anything. How hard it must have been for him – like everyone had turned against him. Yet I remember feeling I'd be disloyal to Mum if I went and she would be alone. No matter what I did, I would be hurting someone.

A few months in, we were at my granny's house when I wandered off from playing with my cousins to find my mum and auntie and granny upstairs in one of the bedrooms. I opened the door before anyone could stop me and saw my mum crying on the floor. I'd never seen her cry before and I panicked. It was terrifying to see her like that. I ran out of the room and it was never mentioned.

My first Holy Communion happened around that time. My chest tightens and my heart hurts thinking back to it. We were going to my granny's house for a party after the Mass and obviously my dad wasn't invited, so his only chance to see me was at the church. He found me with a present, a book of fables, and tried to talk to me and give me a hug, but I couldn't even acknowledge him. I still felt scared of him even though I didn't know why, and I didn't know how I was supposed to be around him. Now when I imagine him going back to my other granny's on his own having been completely ignored, I well up. I don't think I'll ever get over it. I hurt him so badly. As a teacher I see my pupils making their Communions every year and it always brings back these painful memories. The children are so young and innocent in their little white dresses and suits and I think: how the hell did I have such dark and awful thoughts about myself at that age?

Soon after that we were driving somewhere, me and my mum, and she started to cry out of the blue, so I took her old Nokia from her bag and called my granny because I didn't know what else to do. When Granny answered, Mum realised what I'd done and pulled the car over, put the phone down and told me never to do that again.

That's when I decided there was no one in the world I could speak to when I was afraid. Looking back, Mum was obviously going through an awful time and was maybe depressed herself. She didn't speak to me or my brother much during that time and I didn't really see her. My granny, auntie and uncle took it in turns to stay in our house and they left us to school and made our dinner and checked our homework. I cried every night in bed when the lights were off. Because Mum worked in my school, the teachers knew what was going on. I was desperate for one of them to ask if I was okay but they never did.

It's funny because I vividly remember everything about that time even though it's more than a decade ago, but I have no memories of when or how my dad came back to live with us. It could have been any length of time – six months to two years – before he came back, and it was never spoken about. But for me at least a lot had changed in my relationship with my parents in that time. Looking back, I was slightly traumatised by the whole sorry situation and how it had happened, but because no one spoke of it or asked if I was okay, I learnt to keep the sadness inside and turned the negativity and anxiety and blame in on myself. I'm sure my parents thought they were doing the right thing by keeping us away from what was going on between them because we were probably too young to understand. I know that, but it doesn't help how it felt.

I distanced myself from everyone after that, more than I already had, to make sure I kept the dark, horrible thoughts I had about myself inside. All my energy was invested in making sure they didn't show or slip out. It's hard work keeping secrets, especially when you're a child and the secrets are scary thoughts about yourself. It made me tight and tense and constantly on edge, expecting danger at every turn. I couldn't trust anyone and I'd learnt from the adults around me that the rule is we don't talk about difficult things. Everyone stays silent and doesn't speak when they're sad. Now in school we try to teach the children to talk about anything that makes them sad or worried or afraid but I don't remember any of that back then.

This is hard. I don't know if any of the doctors here would recommend this in my already fragile state, but maybe it's a good thing to finally get everything painful and sore I can remember out in the open. This is probably the most useful therapy session I've ever had!

A few other memories have popped into my head while I'm writing. As each fills my mind I realise how long ago they happened and I wonder if I had spoken about them before or shared them with someone would they still haunt me like they do. Anyway, we're nearly there.

One day, when I was about ten or eleven, my dad wanted to watch a match down at the Gaelic pitches and the only game that day was a ladies' match. Before thinking I said, 'It'd be weird for you to go watch the ladies play', and his face dropped suddenly. From that moment on I believed he lost enjoyment and interest and the escape he got from going down to the pitches for a match, and it was all my horrible fault. I am so sorry, Dad.

A year later, on Mother's Day, we had to write soppy letters in school for our mums. Being the conscientious student I was I wrote exactly what every mother wants to hear from their child. We were to share our letters with our mums that weekend, but before that my teacher, unbeknown to me, told my mum (her colleague) that she was in for a treat on Sunday and gave her the gist of my heartfelt letter. Come Sunday I was too embarrassed to give Mum her letter, so instead I made a funny card, which took hours to make. When I gave it to Mum she was upset and angry at me – obviously just disappointed, but I couldn't understand why she hated my card so much and why I always seemed to do the wrong thing. It wasn't until the next day in school when my teacher asked me if she'd ruined the surprise that I realised what had happened.

Finally, in Primary 6 or 7 I came home from school every day for a week saying my friends were being mean to me when they weren't at all. I used the horrible things that I was telling myself in my head and pretended my friends had said them so I could sit on Mum's knee and let her hug me because I didn't know another way to make it happen. I was desperate for comfort and love and warmth but I didn't know how to tell her. Why was it like that? Why was it never okay for me to show affection and ask for help or love?

And so, here we are. It doesn't seem like much when it's laid out like this, but those early events, thoughts and warped 'rules' I developed after each one have left their ugly mark on me and haunted me every day. They've chipped away at my confidence, my sense of worth and my relationships. Each one has led me here. I might be more hopeful for the future if I could speak out and tell people and apologise, but I can't. It's so difficult and painful. I'm holding in so much unresolved blame and anger and guilt and I don't know what to do about it.

I've never thought about any of this in detail before and I'm exhausted and drained now. My face is wet with tears. I know what's happened, I know what hurt; I've even spoken about some of those times to therapists before, but I can't seem to move on or make it better. My mum and dad are the best couple I know now – they are best friends. If they got over what happened, why can't I? What am I supposed to do with all this? How am I supposed to forget and move on?

Day 12

Hospital Number Two

I had to move hospitals last night. A bed became available on a ward closer to home – one that wasn't for over sixty-fives. I'm not exaggerating when I say it's hell.

I arrived in a taxi, late and in the dark, with my suitcase and a nurse from my old ward. I could barely see where we were going outside but inside I was brought through a maze of busy corridors with lights so bright they hurt my eyes and the alarming sound of screaming close by. Even though I didn't know her and had only met her in passing once or twice, I wished the nurse who came with me stayed a while, but she handed over my paperwork and went back to the waiting taxi.

I was led down the hall and it was clear that people don't hide quietly in their rooms here, keeping themselves to themselves like I'm used to. There are people everywhere – men and women, young and old, strange and scary, in every direction. There's a female corridor and a male corridor with the nurses' station separating them. Each side has twelve bedrooms and there's a dark shared TV lounge in the middle that has one ancient fat TV (I didn't know TVs that old still existed) surrounded by three beaten sofas in a square. The sofas are threadbare and dilapidated.

Everyone's eyes were on me as I shuffled behind the new nurse in my pyjamas trailing my suitcase for what seemed like forever to get to my room. There were patients and nurses everywhere, and when I tried to look around, gauging the place, I avoided making eye contact. They were all standing in packs of two, three or four and my arrival was their entertainment for the evening. Everyone, staff included, brazenly looked me up and down; no one even tried to hide their staring.

I caught a glimpse of a group, boys and girls around my age, leaning against the wall outside my room waiting to size me up. They must have known I was coming. The girls were plastered in make-up and dressed to the nines in jeans and strappy tops and jewellery. The boys were wearing Adidas tracksuits and blingy silver rings with cigarettes tucked behind their ears. It was intimidating. I had seen only a handful of people on my quiet, peaceful ward for nearly two weeks and I was shaking with fear. What had I walked into? By the time I made it into my room I was fighting back tears of terror and humiliation.

The nurse was talking about mealtimes and medication but I couldn't take any of it in. She left and I registered my surroundings. I was horrified. It was filthy. It smelt like a damp, lived-in old nursing home and I had to breathe through my mouth to lessen the smell. I was scared to touch anything. There was a used plaster sitting on the shelf and a pot of what could only have been piss in the attached bathroom where the smell was sickening. With one finger I pulled back a corner of the bed's old tatty duvet and to my horror I saw the sheet below covered with hairs and dirt from whoever was last in the bed. There was graffiti on the wall – broken speech about Ian Paisley and the IRA. I was devastated to be here, ripped suddenly from my quiet, clean little room only an hour ago, now alone and afraid. I felt the panic rising dangerously inside me.

Mum and dad came soon after. I'd rung them in panic – angry, blaming them that I'd been moved here when of course it wasn't their fault. I was just angry and upset and needed someone to blame. I stood frozen in shock and cried silently in the corner while Mum and Dad scrubbed the place as clean as it could be. I couldn't speak to them because I was still trying to process how horrific this place was. I was too terrified to even perch on the wooden chair in the corner and it felt like bugs were climbing up my back and into my hair. They brought my blanket and pillow and sheet from home, disposing of the old dirty ones in a laundry room Mum had asked about. I heard the nurse say they had meant to change the bed sheets before I came in but there wasn't time.

The building is so old there's no internet or Wi-Fi, which makes me feel even more cut off from the real world outside. I can't keep in contact with anyone and I've gotten used to watching something on my auntie's iPad to try and pass an hour or two in the evenings. It's going to be harder to keep busy and fill the days here without the distraction of looking stuff up on my phone.

But the worst part is the crowds of people everywhere. When I stumbled my way through the corridors last night to find the office and collect my night meds, I saw a man shouting and swearing at one of the nurses about his medication; he said it was wrong and he wasn't taking it. I swear he was about to swing for her before I ran off in the opposite direction. The patients hang around in groups and act as though the staff are their enemies – they make rude comments, tell them to 'fuck off' and are aggressive when a nurse passes by. Every time I walk past someone I get a whiff of unwashed skin and damp or pissy clothes. One boy came right up, inches from my face, eyes rolling back in his head and asked me for a cigarette.

There's always noise and arguments and music blasting from rooms. It makes me tense and on edge – jumping at every noise and shadow. My body can't relax. It's on high alert, waiting for the next danger. This feels more like a homeless shelter or youth hostel or young offenders' unit than a hospital. My next-door neighbour is a girl called Chloe who came to suss me out shortly after I arrived and asked lots of questions about why I was here and where I'd come from. I fumbled a lot and eventually shrugged and said I get nervous. Even here, surrounded by people that must be in the same boat, I can't admit to depression.

She told me she'd been here for seven weeks. I couldn't believe anyone could be here for that long; being in the last ward for eleven days was bad enough. She's 19 and has a two-year-old boy at home. She showed me a picture of him on her phone. As she showed me I couldn't help noticing her nails – long and impeccably painted, and she was wearing the biggest set of fake eyelashes I've ever seen. I felt disgusting then talking to her with a pale face, my hair pulled back out of the way and tracksuit bottoms on. I haven't thought about making an effort in weeks, way before I came into hospital. I can't remember how to put make-up on now if I could ever be bothered. I'm ugly no matter what and make-up isn't going to help.

I was worried I wouldn't sleep but the whole upheaval and crying for hours left me exhausted, so along with a sleeping tablet, I fell asleep quickly into a black, dreamless sleep and didn't move all night. Most people's lights were still on and shining in from the corridor through the window in my door as I fell asleep.

This morning one of the nurses woke me and told me to come round for breakfast. I didn't know if people got dressed for breakfast here so I pulled a hoody on over my pyjamas and followed a few stragglers making their way round to, I assumed, the canteen. When I got there, again I was amazed at the ridiculous amount of people in such a small space. The canteen was arranged into six round tables with four chairs, four place mats and four sets of cutlery at each. My stomach dropped when I realised I had to sit with these strangers and make conversation. This isn't like the last place where there were only a few of us and I could stay hidden in my room with a tray.

I moved to the back of a queue of about twenty people waiting to get served (half were dressed; half looked like they'd been pulled straight from their beds). There were six or seven nurses sitting on chairs in a line at the far end of the room watching us in silence and I felt like an animal in the zoo. Why did they need to watch us eating breakfast? What happens that so much manpower is needed as people serve themselves cereal? I looked around, avoiding eye contact, for a table I could sit at. I looked for the least intimidating space where I might get away with sitting and not speaking to anyone, but searching the canteen I realised there was no way I could stay here to eat and talk.

I wanted to leave and return to my room with my breakfast like I used to, but I imagined everyone's gaze on me if I walked back through the door to my room with a plate of food. Are we allowed to do that here? I found it impossible to move then and like I was being pushed involuntarily along in a crowded mosh pit with people in front and behind me in the line. I remembered that no one here knows I'm vegetarian, and if I say, the people around me will listen and stare and ask questions and be impatient.

My mind and heart were racing faster than ever before. I felt my throat start to close over and I struggled to get a breath. My hands were damp and sweat was forming on my top lip. My eyes were watering, my whole body felt like it was on fire and going to implode any minute; I knew my face was bright red and my neck and chest were covered in stress blotches. It seemed extra noisy and bright. People were everywhere and I was sure they were noticing what was happening. My breath was catching in my throat like the air couldn't get past the lump that had formed and I knew I hadn't much time to escape without passing out. In that moment it felt as if the walls were coming in on me and the room was getting smaller. I was going to suffocate or be trampled by everyone around me.

I turned in complete panic and bumped into the person behind – a huge man, tall and wide, with a hairy moustache and full shirt, tie and heavy overcoat on. He hadn't been expecting me to move that way and so quickly. A thought flashed by that he smelt like he hadn't showered or washed his clothes in weeks. I tried to apologise but couldn't find the words and half-ran half-walked through the tables trying not to draw attention to myself. I didn't want to imagine the state I looked in front of these people, who I guessed were all now watching me.

Eventually I made it out of the canteen and down the corridor towards where I thought my room was. I hoped I wouldn't meet anyone and, as I was still getting to know my way around, prayed silently that I wouldn't push open a door into the wrong room and walk in on someone getting changed. I wheezed and gasped for a breath, thundering down the hall, thankful that everyone, including the nurses, seemed to be in the canteen.

When I pushed open my door and recognised my own dirty, dark room I whimpered in relief and threw myself onto the edge of my bed before my knees gave way. I gasped and spluttered and made strange heaving noises trying to breathe in and out without much luck. Maybe five – or it could have been 50 – minutes later a nurse appeared beside me trying to talk to me. I assumed she saw my less than graceful exit from the canteen but I couldn't hear her over the pounding of my heart and rapid breathing echoing in my ears. I was wheezing in and out at ten times the normal speed and it was making my head light and woozy. I saw black spots in front of my eyes, like when you look up towards the sun. I think the nurse was telling me to breathe slowly and tried to show me how but I couldn't focus on her because my body was convinced it was dying and no matter how many times she told me to breathe in and breathe out it didn't help. I don't remember the nurse leaving but she must have thought I was ignoring her. Later I'll be mortified that she saw me in that state.

The panic attacks came in waves after that – the worst I've ever experienced, – for two or three hours. I'd get my breathing slower and my heart rate lowered and then have a flashback of everyone staring at me in the canteen or I'd realise that I have to live here, in this place, and the panic overwhelms me again. I shook and wheezed and gripped my chest to desperately suck in any air at all.

Somehow, it's night-time. I've been in this horrific cycle of pure panic since eight a.m. I haven't eaten or drunk anything all day – my throat wouldn't allow it. I haven't even been to the toilet. I've been given a sleeping tablet, but I'm so exhausted from the trauma of today that I'll probably sleep without it. I take the tablet anyway and as my eyes begin to close, I glimpse a text from my mum from three hours ago asking how I got on today. I couldn't reply to her even if I wanted to.

Day 13

Meds

I have to queue for my tablets three times a day at a little window near the nurses' station. In the queue other patients talk to me and ask questions about why I'm here and what hospital I came from. They tell me how long they've been here and why they were admitted. I'm taken aback at how easy they talk of the breakdowns they've had and how many times they've been in different psychiatric hospitals over their lives. I'm shocked at how many people have been admitted time and time again. When I came in I assumed that when I leave I'll be better, but because no one has come near me in the last thirteen days, I've started to think of this place as more of a holding cell when you've nowhere else to go. I hope when I leave here I'll never have to come back.

I was talking to a woman called Alice when we were queuing for tablets. She told me about the boy who left before I came in – the boy whose bed I've taken. He's 20 and everyone loved him it seems. She said he was sweet and innocent and gullible and was always unwittingly getting himself into trouble. As she was telling me about him, she placed her hand on my arm and said, 'There wasn't a bad bone in his body. He was just young and alone and frightened', like she needed me to understand that he was actually good, but then she told me that on his first day of pass – when he was allowed out of hospital grounds – he was six hours late coming back and turned up off his head on drink and drugs. He got kicked out on the spot. I find it hard to believe they would do that, but then again nothing here surprises me. She told me they've heard he's homeless now, living on the streets. Alice is trying to get a number for him off the nurses to contact him and tell him he can stay in her house while she's here. Her tone was urgent – like she's worried something will happen to him. I feel guilty for taking his bed, as if he was kicked out to make room for me.

I'm struck too that she would let him stay alone in her house when she isn't there. She seems sensible but even in my less than stable state I don't think that's a good idea. It's mad how close some of these people become after a few weeks of living together. I'm such a bad person for admitting it but I'm trying to keep my distance from everyone in here. I'm nervous around them, and I suppose I don't want to let myself become like them either – kept here for months, unclean and desperate. But maybe when you've been here a while you let your guard down.

In the line Alice does most of the talking (I mainly nod). This is her third time here in a few months and she's been here nine days this time. I don't ask why she's here, unlike my experience of being here, but it's clear she has an eating disorder. She has the tiniest, most childlike body I've ever seen for a grown woman. The bones in her face are so pronounced you can count every one of them. She looks like a talking skeleton. I'm fat and constantly want to be skinny, just not that thin. But it doesn't change how kind she looks and that when she speaks to you, you feel like the only person in the world who matters.

Later, while I'm shuffling towards the canteen to get a drink, Alice announces that she's allowed to get a taxi to the shop with a nurse and asks if anyone needs anything. She was probably sorry she asked, although she didn't let it show, because about ten patients asked her to get them everything from Lucozade and chocolate to cigarettes and magazines. Thank goodness the nurse was going with her because there's no way she could have carted it all back herself. Most people in here aren't allowed outside the four walls and don't have any visitors to bring them anything. Mum brings me things every day without me even asking.

My doctor's notes from the last hospital say I've to start on the next dose up of my new antidepressant today. I had to tell staff this because I haven't met with any doctors here yet and I doubt anyone has read my notes. This new antidepressant is brand new on the scene (some of the nurses here hadn't heard of it and it had to be ordered in) and gets good results apparently. The doctor from hospital number one told me it's been getting 'great feedback from users', like it's a new piece of tech released to the masses. It's my third or fourth now – hopefully it's third (or fourth) time lucky. I started at just 5mg and it'll be increased over the next few weeks until I'm on the maximum dose I can take. It's usually a slower process but they've said I can speed through the doses quicker than they'd normally prescribe. It could still take up to six weeks if it's going to have any effect, though. I was given a huge list of possible side effects to look out for. The problem with that is you start looking for them. There's been nothing yet, I think, but even if there was, I'd probably stay quiet in case they took me off and I had to start again on a new tablet at a tiny dose.

The anti-anxiety medication they've put me on, however, works straight away. I googled it and apparently it's an anti-psychotic which freaked me out a bit (am I psychotic? I'll ask a doctor if I get to see one again) but I'm desperate, so I'd take anything. I take it three times a day with a double dose at night alongside the sleeping tablet. Around half an hour after each dose things get a bit fuzzy and I can't hold a conversation or focus (more than usual). Sometimes I'm aware I'm sitting open-mouthed and totally out of it but my brain isn't able to send the signals to my limbs to tell them to move. This morning I was so drowsy I couldn't open my eyes fully and had to lie down. It was like being drunk or in a dream, feeling anxious and confused. As I lay in bed, the room spinning slightly, I thought about the pills making their way through my system – including the extra milligrams of antidepressant I'd started. I talked to it directly in my head, as if it could hear me, willing it to work and hoping beyond hope that this is the one that'll stick. I feel like my life depends on this little tablet and I suppose in some ways it does.

How do they make an antidepressant? What do they put in it? How do you make happiness in tablet form? I don't even care for happiness – that seems like too much to ask for. I'd take anything slightly better than this. Lying here, with only moments to go until I feel as high as a kite, I imagine the antidepressant tablet landing in my stomach. I see it dissolving into tiny pieces and flying off in different directions to fix whatever mess is up in my brain; similar to a cleaning team being let loose in a dirty house. Please, little tablet, I pray, do what none of the others could do. Please help me out of this. Please help me feel better.

When I wake a few hours later I'm still thinking about these new meds. My biggest worry is how I'll know if I'm getting better or if these new tablets are beginning to work. I've asked every doctor and nurse but they're always vague. I'm desperate for any clue that things could improve. Will I wake one morning and the big black mass inside my brain will have lifted? If I felt even a tiny glimmer of 'better' sometime soon, it might give me a bit of strength and encouragement to look for the next little glimmer and the one after that until maybe one day those moments won't be so far apart.

A nurse a long time ago told me that things should start to get easier and I'll move closer to how I was before – but the problem is that it has been such a long, traumatic road over so many years that I can't fully remember what it was like before this depression took over. If I do start to get better, I worry I'll be too anxious to say or to admit what could be happening in case I'm wrong or I jinx it. It's unrealistic that I'll become happy overnight; I just don't want to be constantly plagued by my own put-downs and stinging criticisms or maybe not permanently exhausted and crying.

I'm frustrated that I can't shake myself out of this – and frustrated at the doctors and nurses too for not offering help other than more tablets. I feel like I've tried incredibly hard on my own to get better for such a long time but things only got worse. And now I don't have the strength to try anymore. I thought that was why I was brought here – to let someone else take over trying to fix me. If I could get a tiny sliver of peace for a while or if a little of the blackness could subside even for an afternoon, that would be more than enough to give me some hope. Say, if one morning a week I didn't wake up and instantly want life to be over. I don't think that's asking too much.

Every morning now, just as I open my eyes, my mind and body flood with dread and disgust and sadness and grief and anger and listlessness, and my first thoughts are planning how I could die today. It's loud and overwhelming and makes it a struggle to get up out of bed. Sometimes I try to tell the voices 'no', but the depression has grown into such a strong beast that when I try to fight back, the bad bit of my brain responds extra hard and vicious. I don't know why I do this to myself. If I could stop or change it, I would. I've tried over and over but it's bigger than me now and totally out of control. And I believe everything it says too, which allows it to grow. Standing up to it is like trying to force a dragon into a matchbox.

There would be relief, like a weight lifted off me, if I could take back some control and quiet the constant shouting toxicity in my head that picks apart every aspect of my personality and appearance and everything I say and do, and everything that I've ever said and done. Most of the day is obsessing and reliving terrible moments from the past, constant flashbacks, like a record stuck on repeat, of the worst times that make my stomach lurch. If I believed in myself and my ability to recover, maybe I could ignore some of those thoughts and have a little space for peace and quiet. Maybe one day I'll take back some control over my mind and have a bit of input into how I feel and who I am.

My mum comes in the afternoon during visiting and it's a reminder when she goes that she can leave this dirty, horrible place and I can't. I want to scream and punch and kick and rip her hair out in frustration even though she hasn't done anything wrong; I'm just angry today. I've heard how some people with depression, and on certain antidepressants, lose the ability to feel emotions and are numb to everything: no sadness, no happiness, no anger. Would that be easier?

Mum is getting ready to leave and I'm wishing she could do something to help me or get me out of this place. I can't settle here with all the people and how loud and noisy and big and overwhelming it is. I'd got used to the peace and quiet of the previous place where I didn't have to speak to anyone. I ask her to ring someone to see if I can go to another hospital but she says she doesn't think I can go anywhere else. I get angry at her and practically chase her out the door. I get into bed and wrap myself up in a cocoon and beg myself to fall asleep immediately to stop having to think about anything. But I can't sleep – my mind is racing. How on earth does my mum still like me when I'm horrible to her? She always takes the brunt of it. Sometimes I can't hide how awful I feel and it comes out when I speak to her because I suppose I know and hope deep down that no matter what I do she will never leave me and will always love me. My illness is hurting so many people other than myself. Those closest to me must see me as an angry, spiteful, vile person but I can't explain to them that that isn't me. I know I'm still a good, kind person with tons of love to give but my mind takes everything good I have and manipulates it and fills it with poison. It's as if the blackness that's taken over my head and soul needs to spread into the people I love and the things I used to love to survive in me. Yet, somehow, the same few people stand steady, waiting for me with their arms outstretched. I don't deserve any of their love or patience and I can't make myself tell them I love them or thank them for everything they've done for me. That they're still here doesn't make any sense. Then the voice of my depression wakes up and tells me, as clear as if it's sitting in the chair beside me, that it won't last much longer – that everyone has had enough. That they're all ready to turn their backs on me now.

Once a week the nurse gives us a physical – takes our blood pressure and heart rate and records our weight. Sometimes bloods

are taken too. I tell myself not to look down at the scales. It will
be bad news and I want to protect myself from triggering a major
purge but I don't listen and look anyway. I wish they hid the
numbers on the scale but it's clearly written for me and the nurse
to see. I know she's thinking how fat I've got and how ugly it's
made me. I don't hear what the nurse says when she's packing up
to leave because all I can focus on is everything I've eaten today
sitting in my bulging stomach and bursting out of my thighs and
arms and face and I want to throw absolutely everything up from
inside me, organs and bones and all. I know now, thanks to the
nurse, that I've put on a stone since coming into hospital just
under two weeks ago, and although I'd thought as much, with
wearing tracksuit bottoms and jumpers every day and avoiding
mirrors it was hard to really tell. I know I'll be up all night now
fighting with myself to go or stay away from the bathroom and
the toilet. I wonder whether I should go now and get it over with,
rid my fat body of everything I can in the hope that I might stop
obsessing and be able to move on with my day afterwards.

My self-esteem is already rock bottom – I didn't actually
think it could get any lower, but seeing my weight on the scales
is another hard blow that I'm really not up to. After I'd been
weighed, the nurse took my heart rate and remarked that it was
a bit high. I thought, well, duh, I've just been made aware of my
disgusting weight and you know it too, which is embarrassing.

A cleaner comes to mop the floor of my room while I sit on
my bed. She seems nice, trying to make small talk and smiling
at me, but I want her to leave and let me get on with being sick.
She must think I'm horrible and rude, which I don't mean to be
at all. I really don't even want to be sick because it's exhausting
and it hurts and it smells and I haven't for a few days now, but
I'll have no peace until I do.

I spend the next hour over the toilet bowl.

Day 14

The Bathroom

All day long a woman called Kathleen (I know her name because the patients who are aware of their surroundings talk constantly about how she keeps them up at night) screams in pain and howls like she's being brutally tortured in her room by the staff and shrieks incoherent monologues only recognisable by the odd swear word thrown in. It's constant and harrowing and upsetting to hear and I know I'll never get used to it. Her room joins onto mine at the very end of the corridor and I jump a foot in the air every time she wakes up and the screeching starts again. She sounds how my head feels sometimes.

Today the screaming started early – it was the first thing I heard when the nurses woke us up. It seemed particularly loud and unsettling today and there was nothing I could do to block it out or distract myself from the noise. It's been getting worse as the day's gone on. Usually there's some let-up or break – maybe when she naps or is knocked out on meds – but today there hasn't been one minute of relief. She must be in complete distress and turmoil to make those animal-like noises at the top of her lungs, but it's putting me really badly on edge and amplifying everything going on in my head. Selfishly I think that she shouldn't be here, being loud and scary and setting off the other ill and fragile-enough patients who don't need to hear Kathleen screaming all day long. Surely anyone can see it's not fair on her or anyone else? Clearly her 'treatment' needs another look. I hoped I would maybe get used to it and grow to not notice it, like the fan noise in the bathroom, but, no, it's as loud as when I first heard it the moment I walked through the doors.

The screaming around me and the screaming inside my head is intensifying and I feel like I'm being suffocated. I'm struggling to breathe or hear any rational thought above the howls. I can't make it to the canteen for breakfast and then somehow it's lunch, and that seems too much to handle too, and I haven't moved from under my duvet with my fingers in my ears. I try to imagine my insides filled with strong steel, which helps me take two steps outside my door before my heart rate starts to increase and my chest tightens again and the walls close in. Before my door has even closed behind me I turn back into my room and sit on the bed trying to calm myself. It takes a long time to get my breathing back to normal. This is a tough day so far.

On my own I'm left to think, which never ends well. I wonder if Kathleen's screams are actually happening or if I'm imagining them in my head. Can anyone else hear them? This is such a harsh and miserable place that I'm struggling to see how I'm going to make it out alive or with any sanity left at all. I'm saddened by everything that goes on here and I'm trapped in my grey, dirty little room. How is anyone supposed to get better in a place like this? There's no structure to our days here. Not that I expected a jam-packed schedule from morning to night but I thought there would be something. We have nothing to get up for, no reason to get dressed, no help to try and get better. I thought there might be some sort of therapy or counselling or regular check-ins with a doctor or nurse. But nothing, nothing at all. I can go days without talking to anyone.

I'm getting more and more agitated with each second that ticks by. Kathleen has not stopped screaming all morning and afternoon. It's as if she's sitting right beside me on my bed screeching directly into my ears, but I'm alone. And when I put my hands over my ears to block out the noise, the voices inside my head are just as loud and there's no escape anywhere.

I slap myself across my face and punch my legs with my fists. I don't know how I'm going to contain myself much longer. My brain feels like it's pushing out against my head and I worry that it might literally explode. I have an image of screaming and screaming and screaming even louder than Kathleen – louder than everyone in this hospital, everyone in Belfast, everyone in the world, and even then it won't be enough. I try to push it down deep inside me. I have to bite down on my lips to stop them from opening and letting the screams escape. If I start, I don't know if I'll be able to stop.

I go to the bathroom and take the thick shower curtain in my hands, pulling down on it lightly. I'm just testing. I haven't decided anything. I know I should tell someone what's going on in my head but I don't feel like there's anyone who would listen so I keep going. Kathleen and the noises in my head seem to be fading and muted and everything is becoming quieter. It's nice. I might be able to think clearly for a while. I loop the shower curtain up and round and make a knot in it. It looks like a noose. Still my head is eerily quiet for the first time in a long time. I have no thoughts; I'm just playing with the curtain. I'm not actually going to do anything. I make a good solid hole with a strong knot above and put my hand inside. The hole is high enough that I have to stretch up to put my hand in it. The distance between it and the ground is more than the height of me. I pull down and it seems strong, it doesn't move. I place my other hand in it now too and pull down with all the weight I can. It takes it without coming undone or loosening any and the bar it's attached to doesn't even wobble. This is good. It's been such a long time since my mind has felt this quiet. I can't even hear Kathleen anymore. I feel relaxed. My body is on autopilot and my mind is enjoying the peace. I stand up on the toilet seat now and stretch up until my head is resting in the loop on the thick plastic. Looking down, I can see that my feet won't touch the ground if they have to. I push down on my neck and still the bar and loop don't budge. I'm calmer than I've been in weeks – why didn't I try this before? My head is resting in the noose now, swinging like a baby in a crib, and my heels are still planted on the toilet seat. I just need to step off. What would happen if I did?

My friends and family would be upset. I can see them now, gathering at my house, drinking tea and talking about me. I can hear their words saying how sad and awful it is and maybe some of them would even be crying. I can see my mum, inconsolable in the corner, crying constantly as everyone approaches her and tells her how sorry they are and how they can't believe it and if there's anything they can do. I can even see the trays of sandwiches on our kitchen table and the good sets of cups and saucers out for guests. I visualise the church then, a few days later, filled with people from school and home and university and work – people I haven't seen in years dressed in black with solemn faces. I'm there, one of the congregation watching it all. I see a coffin coming up the aisle carried by my brother and my dad and my uncles and my cousins. My mum and aunties follow and I hear Mum howl and I'm embarrassed in front of all these people. I wish some of my friends were behind the coffin too. It's not fair they're sitting in a pew somewhere near the back. My mum would probably never recover – she told me so when the nurse first said I had to come to hospital and she realised how bad things were. She said, her voice shaking while I avoided eye contact, 'You'd never really do anything, would you? You know I'd never come back from that. Promise you wouldn't', I didn't answer that day and I don't remember what happened after.

Surely they know how much I'm hurting? They know this is the only option. They know I'd only do it because I really can't think of anything else. I think they would understand eventually. My friends at least have lives to lead ahead of them, and I hope they wouldn't think about me or what I did for too long after. I imagine myself gone, not feeling anything anymore, not having to do anything or talk to anyone or have any worries. I imagine not feeling any pain anymore. It's nice.

I still have the faces of my friends and family, and now my dog too, in my eyes like they're there in front of me. They're floating heads staring at me and smiling and I might be crying but I'm not sure if that's real because I still have this odd peaceful detached feeling as if I'm floating and I don't feel sad. But I remember my feet now still on the edge of the hard toilet seat and my arms hanging by my sides, my neck stiff against the rough curtain. I realise in that second how easy it is to override the feelings of guilt and sadness and doubt when I look inside myself and see the black and the dark and the ugly, bad part of me that has woken up now and is screaming and screaming for me to step off. Kathleen's screeches start to float back into the room.

The only thing holding me back is fear – fear that it's not the right decision and fear of what comes next. But at the same time I have this urge telling me that this is a good solution for everyone.

The whole scenario in my head has somehow taken only a few minutes although it feels like I've been standing here for hours. The peaceful feeling is gone now. I'm back in the shit, and I still can't think of any other way to fix my brain and stop the thoughts trapped in there than the one facing me right now. I can hear Kathleen louder than before and someone else – deeper, so it must be one of the men, has started howling now too. Somewhere further down the hall there are people shouting, or maybe just talking loudly, and there is music and a blaring TV coming from one of the rooms. Every sound is like a nail being hammered through my skull. I need quiet. I want silence to organise my head and think. Actually, what I really want is to feel nothing and for nothing bad to exist anymore. I'm overwhelmed and weak and exhausted and I could fall asleep right here. I imagine falling into a hole in the ground and being covered over with dirt and mud. No one would ever find me. It's comforting. Desperate to block everything out, I step off the toilet seat quickly before I have time to change my mind.

For a split second the relief is incredible – like a weight lifted off my heavy heart. Did I do it? Am I dead? I marvel at how quick and easy and pain-free it was. But then, in another split second, even quicker than the last, I catch up with the loud crash and bang that's happening and I open my eyes and realise I'm

lying face down on the cold bathroom tiles with my head beside
the base of the toilet. The shower curtain and pole are lying
heavily on top of me and I realise what's happened: a second
bathroom rail taken down.

I push myself up and the pole falls off me. The noose has
loosened until it's nearly open around my neck. I rub my head
where it's pulsing and feel the bump forming above my eyebrow
already. I'm pretty sure I hit my head off the toilet seat when
the shower rail gave out and me, pole and curtain, ended up in
a pile on the floor. I'm still getting my bearings when a nurse,
who must have heard the crash, comes barging into my room
and through to the bathroom (there's no lock). I stumble up to
a standing position as the weight of the guilt of what I've done
catches up with me. I pull the noose over my head quickly and
we both watch it fall heavily to the floor. I need to sit down on
the toilet seat because the bump on my head hurts.

She asks me what happened – as if she doesn't know – and
my instinct is to lie and I tell her the pole fell down. But she's
asking too many questions about how it fell and I don't have an
answer and I can see her looking at me and my head is throbbing
and I know she doesn't believe me anyway, so I admit, like a little
kid being told off, that I made a loop with the curtain and put my
head in it and then it fell. I don't go into any more detail.

She motions to her neck and asks if I've hurt myself. I look
behind her and see in the mirror there's a thick red mark like
a carpet burn across the front of my neck. I put my hand up
to it and it feels hot and raw. I don't know what to say, so I say
nothing. She tells me not to move – which really isn't necessary
because I couldn't even if I wanted to and leaves. I wonder if
I'm going to get into trouble for breaking the shower rail and if
I'll have to pay for the new one. She returns seconds later with
the on-call doctor. It's the first time I've seen him; he didn't
seem to be available until now.

I say I'm sorry about the shower rail, that I didn't mean to
break it, and the nurse tells me it's held up by a magnet, similar
to the curtains apparently, and if a certain weight (like a body, I

presume) pulls on it, it will come undone. I'm mortified. And in my still slightly manic state kick myself because if it had worked, I wouldn't be sitting here like an idiot explaining myself to the nurse and the doctor.

The doctor (after not saying a word to me) and nurse step outside while I continue sitting on the toilet seat, unable to get my legs to work. The nurse returns and I help her carry the shower pole and curtain out of the room. She tells me the doctor has put me on special observation, meaning she'll be stuck to me like glue for the next 24 hours. I even have to pee with the door slightly open and her standing right outside listening. It's humiliating and, even worse, it's self-inflicted and I brought it on myself.

I tell the nurse not to tell my mother or anyone else who might visit. She isn't happy but thankfully she can't go against me because I'm an adult, even if I'm a crazy one. I've made her agree that when my mum comes to visit later I'll meet her at the nurses' station and walk her back there when she's leaving before the nurse takes over so I'm always in sight of either the nurses or my mum and Mum won't know I'm under obs. Hopefully she doesn't use the bathroom and notice the shower curtain is gone.

The nurse makes me hand over my razor and straighteners (they forgot to when I first got here) and I have to walk with her to put them in a locker and then find a chair for her to sit on outside my room. The door is wedged open most of the way and I sit on my bed, always in her eyeline, trying to read and write and nap. We don't speak.

At dinner time I walk to the canteen with my nurse. Thankfully once we're through the door she takes her place at the end of the room with the other nurses, who sit and stare at us in an attempt to save me from the embarrassment of everyone knowing I'm on obs, but it's not enough; news travels fast here and everyone somehow already knows. I thought the other patients, the ones who are aware of what's going on around them, would whisper about me and try to guess what I did, but they're actually sympathetic and give me sad smiles. They tell me how much they hate obs themselves and that it'll be over soon.

I feel guilty making the nurse follow me back to my room with my tray and cringe when I imagine her staring at me in silence while I eat my dinner on my bed. Instead, for the first time, I eat with the rest of the patients at one of the tables. Alice pulls me out a seat beside her and I sit. I don't say much but I manage to get through most of a sandwich and some rice pudding without panicking or needing to leave. I don't hang around, though. The second I'm finished I clear my tray and my nurse follows me back down the corridor.

Later, the nurse is swapped for an older lady. She introduces herself and we have a short chat about the weather (I don't know what it's like because I haven't been outside and my windows are too dark and dirty to see out) and then I start getting ready for bed. When another nurse passes she asks for her iPad to occupy herself while I sleep. The light from the corridor streams into my room because of the propped-open door. The nurse adjusts it a little so that the glare isn't directly on my bed, but she still doesn't lose sight of me.

From my bed I tell her in a small voice that I'm sorry she has to sit there all night, that it must be uncomfortable on that hard-backed chair. She smiles and tells me she's addicted to playing Candy Crush on her iPad, which will keep her busy and she'll be fine. Some time passes and I'm drifting off to sleep when out of nowhere she asks me how I would have felt if it had worked. I'm taken aback at first and wonder if I've dreamed her speaking, but I sit up a little and see her staring at me. It makes sense that she was briefed on why she was stuck to me tonight, but I had nearly forgotten that was why she was sitting there. Before I answer I wonder if it's a test to see how likely I am to do it again, but I check her face and in the light from the corridor I can see there's no hidden agenda in her question. In fact, she looks sad staring at me and I'm not sure if it's the bright light and my tablets kicking in but her eyes seem shiny and wet. I try to really think about my answer because it's nice she asked, I suppose. Would it be sad not to be here anymore or would it be a relief? I can't imagine it. I can't put a feeling to it. This seems like a disappointing answer, so instead I tell her I'm not sure. That seems okay because she nods and goes back to her iPad.

I'm awake now, although I turn onto my side with my back to the nurse because I don't want her to see. The nurses think I'm stupid for trying to kill myself, but they don't understand that I feel like I haven't any other choice. It's been two weeks between hospitals now and if anything, I'm getting worse. It's claustrophobic and chaotic in here and no one seems to know how to make me better or has tried yet. I've spoken briefly to a doctor twice. Each time I'm questioned on my past and then sent back to my room. What's the point?

You know what? If it had worked, I wouldn't be hating myself right now for another failed attempt.

Day 15

Farewell Party

When I wake up there's a different nurse sitting at my door. I have to tell her I'm going into the bathroom to change out of my pyjamas, so she comes and holds the bathroom door open a crack. Thank God I haven't needed a number two in the last day – I'd absolutely die with embarrassment! I change into sweats, don't bother brushing my hair or looking in the mirror and make my way round to the canteen. I'm almost excited to go there today because at least it means the nurse will be more than six feet away from me for a while. Alice is happy to see me, so I sit with her and a few of the others again. I feel relaxed around her. I notice she's pretending to eat from the tiniest bowl of porridge and it makes me self-conscious about my two pieces of toast and jam that I'm hungry for.

Everyone is surprised when it comes up in conversation that I am/was a primary school teacher. I don't tell them I can see the roof of the school I taught in last year from right here, in this spot, in the canteen. It was only five months ago I was there – back in June, pretending everything was okay.

I understand their surprise. I can imagine what they see when they look at me: a weak, timid, fearful little mouse. I know that depression has done this to me. It has ripped me of my confidence and self-esteem and has made me truly believe that I am a disgusting, useless waste of space. I struggle to remember how I was once full of life and fun and could easily lead 30 loud, lively, excited little people every single day. Even harder is remembering that I used to enjoy it too.

Now when I imagine going back to work, I can't remember the happy faces of the children each morning or their pure love for me and their smiles and hugs and happiness, even though I know that happened. Instead, my body floods with dread and an immediate punch of stress and panic and failure hits my gut. I remember the black cloud of marking and assessments and planning and action plans and observations and targets and parents and colleagues and paperwork and how anything less than absolute perfection wasn't good enough. The bad part of me tells me that I'm not good enough. I can't do it; I can't handle that environment and I won't be able to ever again. I'm too weak.

When I left my last school back in October, just over a month ago, I didn't feel like I had a choice because of the rapid and terrifying decline of my mental state. Every day I lost more and more of myself – like the real me was dying and disappearing, and it felt like one morning I would wake up and be completely gone. I told myself when I left that I would go back to work in January, that I was taking a few months to breathe and relax. I know I could never go back to the job and school I left, but at the time I told myself I could sub and maybe tutor and get myself back into it slowly. I was naive to think that this would be over that quickly and that all I needed was a rest.

I'm worried, though, that I'll never go back to teaching. I know when I wasn't as ill I was good at it, but right now I don't think I could do it unless there was some way of not letting it completely overwhelm and swamp me like it has for nearly seven years now, since first year of university. I need to learn to switch off outside school and to settle for less than back-breaking perfection, but I don't know if I'm capable of it. Every evening and weekend I had books home to mark, plans downloaded to improve on my laptop and spent hours sitting at the printer and laminator making extra resources that just might help someone. I became such a painful perfectionist when I realised I was lacking in so many areas. But if I could allow myself some leeway and didn't constantly push myself for unattainable workloads and targets, I might be able to cope better. I can't imagine ever being the same person or teacher I was before because I know I'd end up back here again one day.

Jesus! It's been a quiet day and my nurse left for good a few hours ago but right now it's like I've walked into some ridiculous tragi-comedy. If anyone knew the scenario playing out in here, they'd think I was making it up. I have just had to sign a card for a man's leaving party that's happening later tonight and give two pounds in for frozen pizza and chips from the shop. The man is heading back to prison tomorrow. Christ! I don't even know who he is. I avoid the other patients as much as possible. Also, should we be throwing a party for a criminal? And should he have been living here freely with us for the last few weeks? What if he's a murderer?

Loud, annoying Damien has of course elected himself head of the party committee and the power has definitely gone to his head. My room was a bit of a sanctuary I could hide from everyone in, but, and I don't know how he found out which room I was in but he did, so he's been in here twice today already. The first time he came under the guise of offering me some pickled herrings, which left my room stinking for long after, and the second to get me to sign the 'Sorry you're leaving' card for our inmate. Each time he stayed he talked at me for nearly 20 minutes until I thought I was about to pass out from the exhaustion of listening to his rambling stories that I don't understand. He's very intense and loud and interrupts everything you say and I'm starting to see why I've caught the staff rolling their eyes at him a few times behind his back.

I didn't know what to write in the card to this unknown man and panicked with Damien staring at me, so I wrote my name without a message or anything, which is weird, I know, but I'm the last to sign it so hopefully no one else will see. I purposely went for a shower before the 'party' was due to start to give me an excuse not to answer when, like I knew he would, Damien came knocking at my door to tell me to come join. He's now knocked three times, which means I've had the longest shower of my life, my fingers are all wrinkly and my windows are steamed up. When he hasn't knocked in a while and I think it's safe, I turn off the shower and hear the music from the canteen and someone (Damien) getting up to do karaoke. Shortly after, when everyone is heading back to their rooms and the party is over, I hear Damien pull everyone in for a group picture. They're getting on like a group of drunk mates on a night out, not a bunch of sober patients sectioned together in a psych ward. I get a disturbing image of the nurses sneering and laughing at us from their office, discussing among themselves how tragic and pathetic we are. I ask for a double sleeping tablet before bed.

Day 16

The Patients

Now that I've started spending little bursts of ten minutes here and there in the canteen at mealtimes with Alice and a few of the other patients, I'm finding out a little more about the people I'm living with. Everyone has a story here. Kathleen is the lady who screams all day long, which I already knew, but I have more sympathy for her now despite the headaches she causes since finding out her story. I knew she was bedridden and constantly on observation because there's always nurses in and out of her room, but I've noticed she doesn't get any visitors. Last night she kept everybody awake. At breakfast everyone was complaining and Alice told me that apparently a year ago Kathleen tried to kill herself by setting herself on fire. She can no longer move or talk properly because of her injuries and the burns she's suffered; she's trapped in her body. Apparently she hates the nurses and any of them coming near her or touching her, which of course they have to do. She screams to let out her frustrations and objections because it's the only way she can.

In the room opposite Kathleen is John, who shouts nearly as loud as Kathleen and always repeats the same noises over and over again. They must be placed at the end of the corridor on purpose – maybe to isolate the racket – but they seem to set each other off and, unlucky for me, they're the two rooms closest to mine. It's hard to make out what John's saying most of the time when he's shouting but he curses a lot and that's always clear. I didn't know you could hear and feel that amount of anger and hurt from a person without them saying a word. Yesterday I heard the nurses laughing and mocking his shouts from outside his room, repeating them back to him like a football chant.

Joy's room is opposite mine. She is unnervingly thin and frail and her skin is so pale she's practically see-through. Everyone makes fun of her. She hasn't a clue where she is or why she's here. She has two daughters who come to see her once a week but they never stay long. Joy mutters under her breath constantly, Bible verses and old prayers. If you ask her anything or meet her in the hallway, she quotes lines from the Bible and tells everyone they're a sinner. She checks if people are saved or blessed before she chooses whether to sit beside them in the canteen. She also has a creepy habit of telling people the sins they've committed before bursting into a shrieking laugh without breaking eye contact. I'm not joking – it's terrifying. I try to avoid her.

Avril is in the room next to Joy. She must be at least seventy, the oldest lady here, although she is strong and stubborn and sturdy. She packs up everything in her room every single day, stuffing all her belongings into plastic bags and suitcases, and spends half the morning moving them one by one to the front door. She won't let anyone help or touch her things. She then sits at the door with her walking stick, surrounded by her exploding bags, looking out the window. Despite the nurses and patients repeatedly explaining to her that it's not the case, she still thinks that every day she's going home and waits at the door for someone to come for her. One of the patients told me that she's been here for nearly a year and that she'll probably never leave.

Dale is around my age and greets me with a bow and a 'Namaste' every time I see him in the corridor or canteen. He has huge coloured tattoos on his face and arms and neck that make him look scary, but when he speaks it's quiet and gentle. I've seen him use that quiet voice to be extremely rude to the nurses in the corridor, though – telling them they're fucking useless and haven't a clue. I've never seen his full face because he wears sunglasses all day every day. He told me when we were queuing for meds that he's homeless but has a room in assisted living waiting for him when he gets signed off by the doctors in here and is allowed to leave. I asked him if he would try to get a job on the outside but he shrugged and said no because he gets DLA. He walks with a stick but seems to use it more for tricks than actually walking.

My next-door neighbour, Chloe with the baby, told me a story in the line for morning meds today. It was from when she first got here – about a man who was here a few months ago. He was some sort of genius with a really smart job who was admitted when he had a breakdown. He ordered wire cutters online to be delivered to the hospital (no one checked his parcel when it arrived). It seems he used them to cut a small hole in the fence of the smoking area at the back of the hospital one night when it was dark, and although he had no intention of leaving himself he spread the word among his friends on the ward that it was there if anyone wanted to take advantage. One of the women had seen him cut the fence from her bedroom window and in the middle of the night she dressed herself in black and built a realistic body out of clothes in her bed to fool the nurses doing night checks. She escaped and ran across the fields, not stopping until she made it the whole way home, a good few miles away at least. It wasn't until the next morning that staff discovered she was gone when they tried to wake her for breakfast. They rang the police who, after coming to the hospital to take statements, found her at her own house, in her bed, asleep. She didn't fight them bringing her back – she had just wanted a night in her own bed.

After supper I hear Joy manically laughing from across the hall. One of the nurses was there and Joy was telling her in breaks between her laughter how she had blocked the toilet by ripping up the toilet rolls in her room and shoving them into the bowl. She had broken the toilet and flooded the bathroom and there was water all over the floor. Her ecstasy over what she'd done is scary. I realised later that it was the first time I'd heard her speak about anything other than Jesus. Then, before bed when I was half asleep, I heard John in his room shouting 'UUUU DDDDD AAAAAAAA' over and over again at the top of his voice for a good five minutes. When he finally stopped and it was quiet again, someone from somewhere down the corridor (probably Damien) shouted 'UP THE FUCKIN' RA' which set John off again for another hour.

Day 17

Glimpsing the Future

There was a mouse in the corridor outside my room this morning. Chloe and I came out of our rooms at the same time to see what the shouting was about and it ran past Chloe and hid under her bed. She screamed and one of the cleaners, a big Polish man with little English, went into the room and stamped on the mouse hard. I heard and saw the crunch and squelch before I realised what he was doing and could look away. I felt sick but Chloe was delighted. The cleaner came out of the room a minute later and held up the bin bag he'd swept the mouse into. He pointed at it with a nod and said, 'Mickey dead,' then continued to clean.

Sometimes I now venture out of my room to the canteen in between mealtimes when it's quieter and there are fewer people about. Most of the time the canteen is locked but sometimes it's left open so I can get a paper cup of tea and take it back to my room. Joy was sitting there on her own this afternoon and I felt bad for her, so I decided to stay and sat beside her. Even though her face lit up when I sat down, I regretted it immediately when she took my hands in her cold, clammy fingers and tried to pray with me. She thinks we're friends now – ever since she has been coming to my room to show me things like prayer books with her notes scribbled over them and crucifixes with bits of paper stuck over Jesus' private parts, which she did herself. I never let her past the door, God forgive me, for I know if she came in, she'd never leave. Also, I know she's old and sick but she scares me a bit and I don't want to be on my own with her.

She has just left my door again, disappointed this time because I wasn't able to tell her about any visions I've had of the Lord and Mary. She means well but she's completely out of touch with reality and I haven't met anyone like her before. I know she'll never get better – she might even die here. Five minutes after she'd left me for about the fifth time this afternoon, she began shoving hand-drawn pictures of Jesus under my door, and when I left my room for supper I nearly stood on an orange she'd left for me on the floor in the corridor as a present.

Mum came in today to drop off clean pants and pyjamas. I told her I didn't think I wanted to go back to work this school-year. As soon as the words were out of my mouth I readied myself into defence mode but was shocked and surprised when I didn't need to – she said it was a great idea. I couldn't say anything else then because I was caught off guard and my eyes started to water and a lump formed in my throat. It wouldn't have changed my decision if she'd disagreed or tried to talk me out of it, but I just wasn't expecting her to go along with it so readily. I suppose I forget sometimes how sick I must be. I'm getting used to being here, but it maybe seems more obvious to Mum when she has to leave her normal life to come to this place every day. I feel guilty too for assuming she wouldn't have supported my decision. I should probably try talking to her more and trusting her. I'm usually too afraid and embarrassed even though that wasn't too bad really. I bottle the good feeling from sharing something I was worried about and promise myself I'll do it again. I can relax a little more now knowing I can forget about going back to work until next September.

Following that decision, I start to think about how I'll fill my time, without a job, when I get out of hospital. I clearly didn't do the first few weeks out of work properly because I ended up here. I'll need to try something different. Maybe I can keep myself busy and distract myself out of this. But is that really solving anything or just ignoring the problem? I always wanted to take a gap year after university where I imagined I would travel and sunbathe and relax for a few months, but the thought of packing bags, navigating airports and leaving the country makes my insides crunch and churn at the things that could go wrong far from home. That's not how I used to feel. I used to be brave and adventurous and not afraid of anything. I would have gone anywhere and always had somewhere on my list. I know I have a long way to go to get back to that.

I borrowed my phone charger a few days ago and decided to be bold and not give it back like I was supposed to. Instead I keep it plugged in by my bed. No one has come to take it back and none of the nurses have noticed I still have it or have asked for it. I was sure the staff would say something when they came into my room but they didn't, so I think it's safe now and I can keep it here for good. A little part of me had to look inside myself and check I wasn't planning on doing anything bad with it like before – and maybe I should give it back to be safe, but I surprised myself because where I used to see it as a weapon and the means to an end if I needed it, now it doesn't hold the same threat and I don't have that overwhelming urge I had a week ago. I'm not sure what's changed. Surely it's too soon for the medication to be having any effect. Is it writing everything down in this little book? Or starting to talk to some of the other patients? I'm not sure. All I know is time has moved on and right now the pull to do something dangerous isn't as strong as before. I might risk it and ask for my straighteners later and see if I can keep them too without anyone noticing.

I'm annoyed now – the man serving lunch has pissed me off. I always go and have a look at what's on at lunch and dinner time even though most of the time it looks gross and like it's been festering under the weird lights for days, but I go anyway for something to do and because occasionally there's something edible. It's never a good omen to start with when it's this guy serving because, number one: he has a gross grey beard thing that hangs like a scruffy triangle off his chin and that I bet sheds into the food, and, number two: he slaps the food onto the plates in the messiest, slushiest way with juice and bits always running off the edges and making it look even more unattractive than it already is.

But today, surprisingly, there's a vegetable thing I could stomach and save Mum the hassle of bringing something up later. But by the time I got to the top of the queue he had given away the full tray despite there being sausage rolls and ham for the non-veggie patients to choose from. I asked anyway if there was anything vegetarian (I know I'm the only veggie here) and he looked surprised even though we've had this conversation many, many times now and pointed to the empty tray like, oops. I stood there awkwardly until he said there were sandwiches in the fridge and offered me a choice of chicken or turkey. He stared at me and I thought he actually might have been joking until I realised he was serious, so I turned and walked away.

As I'm writing this I know it's a bit all over the place going from, say, suicidal thoughts to lunch, but that's a bit like every day in this place and in my head too. Every time I meet someone in the corridor or queuing for meds or in the canteen I need to take some alone time after to process who I've met and what I saw and what was said, but my head is in too much of a mess to think properly at the minute and so it's easier to write it down. My brain appears to only function at snail speed except when I'm beating myself up over something and then it speeds into overdrive. It seems to help having this book – somewhere to put these sometimes manic but mostly menial thoughts down. I can work through them then at a slower pace to help me keep going and see what's real and what's being manipulated by the poison in my head. I was reading back on a bit I'd written a week ago that said how I look like a monster, and now reading it back I can see that's not fair and not totally accurate. It helps me feel a little more in control and a little less afraid. It's one of the only things right now that I find I can do and feel relatively relaxed for a while. I know I'll probably never read the ramblings in this book again and neither will anybody else, but it's nearly like having a friend I can offload everything onto – every weird encounter, every negative thought or every unwelcome blast from the past, which has been happening a lot lately; random unpleasant memories springing up from buried deep down in my subconscious when I'm trying to find some peace.

I don't trust the thoughts in my head because nothing feels a hundred per cent right at the minute, so it helps seeing things written down in black and white where I can think about them. There's nothing much to do in here, only think a lot anyway, but writing in this shiny little notepad, I know there's no judgement. I know I don't have to hold back and I don't have to put on a front for anyone. I've never kept a diary before, which I suppose this is, and I'm finding it's helping to pass the days.

I finally saw the doctor – only because I forced myself to ask a nurse at breakfast if I could. I just don't understand what exactly I'm supposed to be doing sitting in this place alone every day. How is that helping? Am I missing something? I was beginning to think the nurse had forgotten to pass on my request until a scary doctor lady with a student trailing after her came to my room an hour ago asking why I wanted to see her. Five minutes later I wished I'd kept my mouth shut. She couldn't have made me feel any worse or more stupid and ridiculous and worthless if she'd tried. She was defensive and abrupt, cold and intimidating, patronising with everything she said. Every time I tried to answer her questions she talked over me and shut me down until I felt so embarrassed and weakened and humiliated that I couldn't speak anymore. I stared at the floor until she left. The student cowering behind her gave me a sympathetic look before running out.

I cried then. I felt angry at myself and frustrated for being too emotional to explain or stand up for myself. I am totally dreading having to see or speak to her again. I know in my head what I feel and what I needed to say but it's like there's something missing and I can't translate my thoughts into words. Where has the confident, smart person I used to be gone? Will she ever come back? While I was sobbing, a nurse came into my room because I'd missed dinner and for the first time I felt like someone here was listening to me. She agreed that nothing has happened in the time I've been here and she promised to get me someone to talk to so that I can try to move past whatever is holding me back and keeping me sick. When she left I felt lifted in a way I hadn't for a long time, and when my friend came to visit afterwards I felt a little better and not as hopeless. We went for a short, slow walk around the grounds and although it was cold it felt good to move and stretch and get some air. I felt lighter and less burdened for a little while. I have to hold on to that moment tight as it was rare and fleeting – in fact, I didn't know that could still happen for me. When I picture it again now I can still remember what it felt like.

Day 18

WRAP

Damien was annoying Avril when she was waiting by the door to go home like she always does. Apparently she'd had enough of him, grabbed her walking stick and whacked him hard on the leg. Even better is that at the start she didn't have her stick with her, so while he was talking her ear off she interrupted him and asked him to be a dear and go get it for her, and when he came back with it she used it to hit him! She must have some sense left in her to have orchestrated that. Damien is going round limping and telling anyone who'll listen that he was attacked. The limping leg keeps changing, though.

I met the OT for the first time today. I know she's disappointed in how little we got through and I'm annoyed with myself. I was trying hard but it's like I can't speak today – as if my brain has switched off and left me to flounder without it. She wanted me to start this thing called a WRAP. She talked about it for ages and made it sound like some sort of magic wonder treatment. I couldn't concentrate because she went on and on about it so I zoned out for a while but I don't think she noticed.

After the lengthy introduction I thought it was going to be something exciting and new and innovative and I felt hopeful until she showed me a photocopied booklet with questions to answer – that's literally it. Disappointed is an understatement. It asks you to list triggers – things that can be bad for your mood, or signs that you're becoming unwell. I guess the thought behind it is that you read it when you feel bad – I'm not quite sure. Anyway, today she wanted to get the first few questions out of the way. We started the first page, which was to make a list of things you enjoy. I raked my lazy brain and thought of one thing: taking a shower and washing my hair, then got stuck. The OT waited for the next thing but nothing came. I got wrapped up thinking surely there's something else I enjoy, but I couldn't think of anything and we sat in an awkward, uncomfortable silence.

I didn't even notice the tears at first but then the crying got harder and I was frustrated with myself and my head for being so useless at everything. I felt embarrassed because the OT looked around my age and I was thinking, 'God, she must think I'm an absolute state', and I started to get hot and panicked that I wouldn't be able to ever stop crying. I had to try really hard to get my breathing under control, and while I fell apart the OT continued to stare at me without speaking and offered me a tissue. I think the tears were coming too because as well as the embarrassment and panic and frustration, I was annoyed and disappointed – was this all we were going to do? Write some lists? Was this how she thought she was going to help me? It's been weeks now and still no one has suggested anything meaningful or offered any help other than stronger medication.

Finally she gave up and I limped back to my room after fifteen minutes instead of the hour session we were supposed to have. She said we'd try again in a few days' time when I was feeling better. I nodded but didn't say anything because I don't hold much hope for the next time either. (As it turns out, she never came back to try again.)

My mum and auntie came to pick me up because I was allowed out of the grounds. I think the doctor recommended the nurse arrange me an hour or two away from the hospital. It would have been nice if she'd discussed it with me herself or explained why. Mum said we could get lunch and suggested somewhere close by and quiet. I hoped it would be deserted, it being a weekday afternoon. We parked outside and I looked in the cafe window.

At first I felt relieved because there were only two people sitting at a table in the corner, but then, at the same time as Mum, I realised we knew them – they were our old neighbours I had grown up with. My mind shot to standing in front of them being quizzed about what I was up to and why I was off school and also probably why I look like shit. We turned the car around and left without me even having to explain, but I was shaken by the almost encounter. The pure fear that people would see or speak to me or ask questions about work or how I am was enough to tip me over the edge. I felt overwhelmed and exhausted, so we went straight back to the hospital and I lay in bed and beat myself up over how weak and worthless I am until I fell asleep.

It's a relief coming back to hospital, even if I was only away for ten minutes, because despite how horrible it can be, at least I know I'm safe and there's no expectation to be 'normal'. Sometimes in here I feel invisible but I like it because I know no one is looking at me. Other times I get frustrated because I'm not seen or heard. I know that's a contradiction and it doesn't make sense.

In here I don't stick out like a sore thumb, which is how I feel in the real world. Everyone here has their own problems to worry about and their own voices in their heads keeping them busy. I constantly tell myself I am nothing, I am useless, I am repulsive, and I believe that with all my being. I think that not only can everyone else see how disgusting I look on the outside, I'm convinced they can see how rotten I am on the inside too. How could they not see that when it's obvious? It's like that Roald Dahl quote – thinking lovely thoughts that shine out of your face meaning you'll never be ugly, but the opposite.

I'm still in bed, exhausted after venturing out earlier, with the lights off and the curtains pulled and I'm angry at myself (again). I'm imagining what might have happened if we'd ventured into the cafe earlier and spoken to our old neighbours. Imagine I was brave enough to tell the truth? Why can't I just admit that things aren't good right now – that I'm not working or feeling great? It isn't something I could say without fearing I'd make the other person uncomfortable and worrying they'd only ever see me that way even if I got better and moved on. And what can anyone say if I do tell them? From past experience, no one ever knows what to say, and it isn't fair to put anyone in the position of having to come up with an appropriate reply. Everything that's happened is personal and painful and cloaked in shame. I wish I could be brave and unashamed of my illness, like I know I would be if I was physically sick. But I think there's a belief that depression is something you can control, so it's your own fault if you have it and can't get rid of it, which makes it so difficult to admit to and makes me feel ashamed and embarrassed.

I'm not at the stage where I can admit how bad things are to anyone but myself, yet I hope everyone else who feels like me can. I have one set of rules for myself: stay silent, struggle alone, never let anyone know you're struggling; and a different set of rules for everyone else: you're amazing even if you can't see it! Tell someone how you feel! You can get better! You deserve to recover! That's what I tell Alice and Dale when they put themselves down (I never tell them how I feel, so they never have a chance to reciprocate). Maybe one day it won't seem like the scariest thing in the world to admit. Maybe one day I'll put myself first.

I haven't moved now for over five hours and it's nearly bedtime. There's no point forcing myself up now. The ward is really outdoing itself tonight with John and Kathleen kicking off from their rooms up here and a few other deep voices going mad from down in the men's section at the other end of the corridor. Hurry up, little sleeping tablet, and knock me out already.

Day 19

Starting to Talk

I was sitting with Dale at lunch today when a boy around our age, Max, came and sat with us. He had a swollen fist that was black and blue. Dale asked what had happened and Max said that he had punched a wall hard in his room earlier out of frustration when the nurses put him on special obs. He said he'd told them he was fine and didn't need to be under observation but they said they were worried about his mood and attitude. He's worried it'll go against him at his next review with the doctor because he's hoping to get discharged and move into a flat the Housing Executive have set him up with. He only sits with us for a few minutes before he's up and pacing the corridor outside the canteen with his nurse following close behind. I'm worried he'll turn round and smack her in a minute. She needs to give him more space – surely she can see he needs room to breathe. She doesn't have to mimic his every step; it feels like she's purposely riling him up to get a reaction. It's so intrusive being on obs, especially when, like Max, you don't think it's fair or you need it, which means he's extra angry and agitated because he doesn't understand why. The nurses often treat us like we have no say over what we need in here – I'm not even a hundred per cent sure what medication I'm on anymore or why, but surely if they listened and tried to work with us they would see we have the best insight into ourselves. We're still adults even if we're ill.

It's putting me on edge watching Max pace like a caged animal. Having to keep the door open while you pee is humiliating enough, but a nurse trailing you and sitting outside your door means everyone knows what's happening too, which adds to the embarrassment and shame. They've told Max he'll be on obs for twenty-four hours before a review and I don't think he gets a say in how that goes. He needs to try and keep his head or it'll be an easy excuse for an extension. He goes outside to the smoking area for a cigarette and I hear him swear under his breath when the nurse follows him out too.

I'd never really spoken to Max before, just seen him in passing but he was nothing like I'd imagined. I've been surprised by most people in here when I actually speak to them. I was so wrong about them. There is kindness and goodness in every single patient and I'm ashamed of how I judged them at first. I take back everything I said and thought about them. It makes me tear up when I think of how vulnerable everyone is here. I see them share their last cigarettes with strangers, avert their eyes and give a quiet pat on the back to whoever starts crying during dinner in the canteen, and quietly move to get a nurse without making a fuss when someone lies down in the corridor and starts to beat the carpet. They are the most non-judgemental people I have ever met.

When I first moved here I laughed at Joy along with the others for her crazy Jesus talk, I was freaked out by Dale and his scary face tattoos and I was exasperated by Damien's constant need for attention. I thought I was better than everyone else here and I was sure I didn't belong somewhere like this. I did the thing I'm terrified of happening to me: I looked down on these people as 'mad' lost causes with nothing to offer. I was scared of them and thought I was different.

I'm ashamed of myself and glad to have been proven wrong. I am no better than anyone else here – we are all the same and I can see parts of myself in all of them. We are each broken and sad and anxious and need help. I'm sure there are so many people like us on the outside too. If this place does nothing else for me, at least it has given me a better sense of humility and compassion for others in distress. I was selfish when I came here – wrapped up in myself and my own problems without a notion for what anyone else could be going through. I thought I was the only person in the world to experience a depression like mine, but I recognise the silent pain on every person's face in here. It's like looking in a mirror.

I go to the canteen once or twice a day with everyone else now, unless I'm having a bad day, and I try not to hide away in my room like I did a week ago. I thought I'd be happier on my own but I have started to need some interaction with other people. It doesn't feel like the staff want us to speak to each other and it's definitely not encouraged but at meal times they can't stop people from talking to whoever sits beside them.

So I talk to people more now, ask how they are and want to know their answers. When they ask, I tell them what I can about myself in return. I'm still not able to fully open up about myself and my feelings but it gets easier every day because no one around me shies away from it. The patients here are doing way more for me than any of the doctors or nurses have done. I have made friends here. They make me feel like I belong and I don't feel so alone. They don't judge me when I cry or have a panic attack or can't leave my room. They don't need to say anything at all.

They make it easier to get up in the morning when I know I'll be distracted for a while over breakfast. Earlier, I sat around a table with three people I never would have met on the outside. There's Mark who is kind but so sad – you can see it in his face even though he always smiles and says hello to me. He seems to have been in every hospital in Northern Ireland and ranks them on how good the food is in each. He says the last place he stayed had such good food he put on nearly three stone in the six weeks he was there. He hasn't been allowed to see his baby boy or partner in the month he's been here, but he speaks to them on the phone every night and always talks about them.

There's lovely Alice who has an ex-partner on the outside stalking her and terrorising her at her house and where she used to work, phoning and texting her and showing up at her door every other day. The stress has made her unable to eat for months. She is skin and bone. I've never seen anyone as thin in real life and I'm not sure how she can even hold herself up. But she sees the good in everyone and always finds a way to pass compliments on things the rest of us have overlooked. I have saved up every nice thing she has ever said to me because they seem genuine coming from her and so she must really think they're true.

Dale came here voluntarily, which I couldn't believe when he first told me, but now I know it's because he didn't have anywhere else to go. He showed me his old student card from Jordanstown University where he looks completely different without his face tattoos and shaved head and dark glasses. He is actually smiling in the picture. He had started training to become a social worker but got kicked out of the house by his mum for smoking weed. Everything went downhill from there.

But no matter what the story and why and how we all have come to be here, everyone struggles inside their head all day long, despite how hard we try to forget and engage with each other to distract ourselves. The pain is tangible. It fills every room and every corridor. I even see it reflected in the faces of the visitors who enter here terrified of us and counting the minutes until they can leave again. Everyone is suffering here and it makes for a sad, suffocating place to be most of the time.

Patients have come from every corner of Belfast and beyond, all ages and experiences, yet we're here for the same reasons. No one is immune to this disease. Unfortunately, no one I've met has got better or recovered while they've been here. No one has anything positive to report or has undergone any sort of treatment within these walls. It is what I suspected – a holding ground where the only good thing is that it's harder to kill yourself. I think of the millions of people, including those in my own life, who didn't get the right treatment, weren't able to be saved and eventually took their own lives. I should be more grateful to be here. Maybe I am one of the lucky ones.

Two medical students came to my door, brought by Scary Doctor Lady who said I have 'a very interesting history' and would I mind relaying it to them. She definitely said that to butter me up and it worked because I was flattered and felt I'd done something cool and that I could actually teach these students something. Not that I had a choice anyway because I knew she wasn't asking. She was probably looking them off her tail for half an hour. They were only two or three years younger than me – a girl and a boy, and the boy was so ridiculously beautiful that I wished I had showered or dressed today. I made myself promise not to come across too nuts or sad or weird.

They asked me about the months, weeks and days that led to me being brought into hospital. Then they asked about the suicidal thoughts, or 'ideation' as the girl student called it, and what they're like now. I tried to explain that it's me – it's my voice, like a constant rhetoric holding me down, slapping away any confidence or self-esteem that might try to rear its head once in a while. I tried to put into words how exhausting and stressful my days are because I have to try so hard not to listen to the thoughts and try to distract myself so I don't give in to them. They ask me what it is I'm saying to myself. I'm always embarrassed to say it aloud because who wants to tell strangers your deepest darkest thoughts about yourself? But I admit that it's always a variation along the lines of 'you're ugly, you're fat, you're disgusting, nobody likes you, you should kill yourself'. A constant, vicious loop. There's rarely any relief from it – it's relentless, and the more I try to ignore it the louder the shouts become until I can't do anything other than agree and do what they tell me: stay inside, not talk to people, beat myself up. I don't want to look at beautiful student boy then because I know he's looking at me thinking that, to be fair, the fat and ugly thoughts at least are true.

I tell them that some days the thoughts are so loud and aggressive they permeate everything I do and anything I try to achieve. Those are the worst days, when I accept every cruel word I unleash on myself and can't even try to escape them.

Those days they slice right through me and leave such mental and physical exhaustion. They terrorise me and chip away at every part of my existence until I have nothing left. Those days I can't fight back and it's easier to give in and let them engulf me. That's when I usually close the curtains, turn off the lights and go to bed. I try to sleep to hurry the day up, get it over with and turn off the thoughts for a short reprieve. I do this to protect myself from the urge to do the more dangerous things my thoughts tell me to do – that everything would be better if I wasn't around, how relieved everyone would be if I was gone and how peaceful it would be to silence the abuse in my head.

I tell them that 'good' days are when I can live alongside the thoughts, live despite them, and I can function to dress, shower, leave the house. I can't enjoy things or feel happiness or at ease on those days, but they are more manageable. The better days are still tainted with thoughts like 'this won't last' or 'who are you kidding?' and there's a constant sense of fear and anxiety because I know it's only a matter of time before the negative thoughts push their way back to the forefront, and what if they're worse this time? What if this time I can't escape and I give in to the dangerous urges? And so, like a self-fulfilling prophecy, eventually I'm overpowered again; my thoughts spiral quickly and to such terrifying levels of darkness that my brain cannot cope. I try to sleep it off, which reinforces that I *am* weak and worthless and unable to do anything, and the whole cycle starts again but each time it's worse because the thoughts now say, 'See? See what happens when you try?' It's on those days that the thoughts are far stronger than I could ever be, and when you're up against that for days and weeks and months and years, that's when suicide becomes the only beacon of hope for relief.

The students nod and scribble things down. They seem more interested than any fully qualified doctor I've met in here, which encourages me to keep talking and telling the truth. They ask me how I used to be before depression and I tell them I was confident and loud and motivated and interested and excited for the future. I had so much life and love and hope in me. I was

enthusiastic and funny and always in the middle of everything.
I can see them looking at me now, at this anxious shaking lump
of a person, thinking it couldn't be true, but I know it is. It
feels like that person has died. I can't imagine ever being able to
return to that. When I was that person I was carrying a lot but
I was still able to enjoy things and function and distract myself
from the bad thoughts. But I don't even need to become that
person again – I'm not aiming for that level of freedom from
this. I just want to recover enough to go back to having some
sort of life and not be in such pain every day.

The students then ask me about what I've tried to get better.
The list is long. It includes CBT, talking therapy, counselling,
online depression and bulimia courses, monthly GP check-
in appointments, different antidepressants to their maximum
doses, yoga, running, the gym, a puppy. I even paid for a day
retreat once where we spent the whole day in silence and had to
hug trees and hold hands with strangers.

More times than I can remember I've rung Lifeline in crisis
who have each time talked me out of suicide for the night. I've
been to every doctor in my practice, the out-of-hours surgery
and A&E. I have relaxation and mindfulness colouring books, a
SAD lamp that I sat under for an hour every night for a month.
I've started a gratitude diary, I bought jigsaws, meditation tapes, I
had massages, I lost weight, I put on weight. I went on holidays,
I kept meeting friends, I did deep breathing, I listened to music.
But still, inside me despite all this and through everything, I
have stayed grey and sad and looking to suicide. It's frustrating
when you're doing what everyone tells you to do but still aren't
fixed. I have always been motivated to get better and try my very
hardest, up until the months that led to me being in here. By
then I had lost that motivation and didn't want to try anymore.
I tell the students that even now I would try any of this and all
of this again over and over if someone told me it would help.

They say good, that it's good I still want to try. They say this
shows I am hopeful for recovery, but I know they're wrong.
It's not hope, it's desperation. It's knowing that this is my last

chance. These last few years have stripped me of any last ounce of dignity I had. I cannot meet the eye of anyone or hold a conversation anymore because I'm screaming in agony and terror inside. Even though it's in my head it pains me physically too. Like nails down a blackboard, it's excruciating and exhausting and I must be close to dying from it. And that thought brings a relief I'm ashamed and afraid to admit because if I ever say it out loud, the doctors think it's failure. They don't think I'm trying to fight it and that's what hurts the absolute most. Because I *am* trying, but I just can't fight any harder. I am not in control anymore – this is what people fail to understand. If I could stop it and get better I would, but it has completely taken over. Every day is a struggle and I'm left with nothing. No one knows what's happening inside me and I find that saddest of all.

But I'm still here. I find it difficult to explain that I *don't* actually want to die, but I can't go on living like this. I want to laugh again until my cheeks hurt and my stomach aches but instead all I can do is cry for so long that my body convulses and my eyes become sore and cracked and swollen. I want to climb into a dark hole in the ground and hide from everyone. I want to never be seen or spoken to again. There should be more to life than wanting to disappear.

Days are long and slow here, which means I'm shamefully enjoying giving the students the gory details and get some guilty pleasure and amusement at them trying to hide their shock as I describe my run-ins with the car and the shower rails and the thoughts of knives and belts. After speaking to them, although racked with nerves and fear over opening up to more people and remembering and relaying the very worst days, in comparison I don't think I feel the extreme low I did then. But even writing that sentence scares me and I want to rub it out quickly for fear of jinxing it and getting ahead of myself. But I must admit it's true – scary but true. There are tiny fleeting flashes of light I've noticed sometimes sneaking through the curtains recently.

I thought admitting my struggles was the hardest part but, surprisingly, admitting I could be getting better is as, if not more, terrifying. I suppose because there's such pressure to get better. Not just my life but my family's lives depends on it. I search around inside my head to judge if it's true – could I be feeling better? And I decide that although I still can't say I see a future exactly, and I don't know how I'll feel tomorrow or even in an hour from now, I can say that right now, at this moment, I don't want to hurt myself, I don't want to die, I want to be happy and alive. I just need to get there. I don't rub this out – it's probably a good thing to write down. I can look back on this when I need to. I can remind myself that it happened and I felt it somewhere deep inside me and it could happen again.

After the students leave I text my friend, who's also a student doctor, and give her the boy student's name. Within minutes she finds him on Facebook (I deleted social media years ago; the stress of presenting myself as happy and thriving was too much – but clearly it has its advantages). I decide I'm too crazy for the young student and it would go against proper student–patient boundaries. Instead, we decide that my doctor friend can have him – until after a little more digging she finds he has a girlfriend. Typical! I tell her there are always students in here and I'll find her another one, I'm sure. We laugh together over text and it's the closest I've felt to my old life in weeks.

Day 20

Strange Days

I spoke to Adam, the youngest patient here, today at breakfast. He's 18 and painfully quiet. He wouldn't look at me initially but after a while I could tell he felt a little more comfortable and even half-smiled at me for a second before he caught himself. He told me he'd finished his last year in school and he's been here for over two weeks now, just before I arrived. His mum and dad come to visit him every day and his granny and granda came for a visit once too. I already knew this – I remember him showing them around the hospital one afternoon as if he were giving them a tour of his new student house. They, for their part, pretended not to be too freaked out to be here.

I wasn't expecting him to be as posh and well-spoken. I was taken aback although I tried not to let it show. He sounds like he's well-educated which makes me think probably rich. I hadn't thought about really wealthy people suffering with their mental health and being locked up in a run-down miserable place like this. It's stupid of me because of course money doesn't make you immune – anyone can have depression, no matter the size of their house or bank balance. I guess I just assumed that people with loads of money would be able to find better help than this. Maybe this is all there is. I wonder if Adam's accent is part of the reason he doesn't speak much – he doesn't exactly blend in with the thick Belfast accents. Not that it means anything, and

I hope he doesn't think that. The moment Adam loosens up a little, Damien barges over and demands attention for his story about how he took a funny turn in the shower this morning. Immediately Adam jumps in fear at the huge presence and sheer volume of Damien and retreats into himself. I think he'll let me talk to him again, though.

Lovely Alice was discharged home yesterday but she is back already. I see her at dinner and she tells me she just couldn't do it – she couldn't even sit down in her own place because she was so racked with nerves and couldn't stop shaking. She says the whole awful experience with her stalker has really knocked her already rock-bottom self-confidence and being sent home set her back further because it was obviously too soon and probably did more harm than good. It upsets me that she was discharged when anyone can see she is far too vulnerable and ill to go home and live on her own. She looks stressed now even though she's trying to put a brave face on. She played about with a single piece of brown bread at dinner without actually eating any of it. I saw the nurses go into her room with a set of scales to weigh her afterwards.

Another woman went home earlier. I hadn't spoken to her much but Alice told me she had a baby a few months ago and was suffering postnatal depression. Alice says there was 'an incident' with the baby in the bath that led to the mum being in here. I didn't want to know anymore. Before she had even left – she was still by the door moving her bags – the nurses were already moving a man called Brian into her room. His speech is slurred like he's drunk and he's almost impossible to make out when he speaks. I don't think he has any teeth. He scares me because he's unpredictable. He has these sudden mood swings where he'll be muttering happily to himself and then start swinging and shouting at nothing. He's already squared up to people, cornering them like he's about to fight them when they haven't even been speaking or looking in his direction. He has a big male nurse flanking him constantly. He wants to talk to everyone, it seems, so I go to my room and hide, praying he won't push through my door.

There is a man from Romania, I think, who limps around the corridors for hours at a time like a zombie. His eyes are half-open and he doesn't speak or seem to see or hear anybody – it's like he's sleepwalking. Most of the time his mouth hangs open and drool runs out onto the floor leaving little puddles where he goes, but today was totally different; for the first time he seemed awake and he was angry. He appeared bigger and wider than I'd ever seen him, banging hard on the nurses' station door when we were lining up for dinner-time meds. He was shouting angrily in his own language and his hands were tight fists. He kept banging on the door and shouting but the door was locked and the nurses inside ignored him. Damien, who has to get involved in everything, called over to him that most of the nurses were busy doling out medication if he could wait, but he shouted over his shoulder at Damien and even though it wasn't English I could tell it meant 'fuck off'. The banging on the door continued and the shouting got even louder. He's a big guy with clearly a lot of strength when he's awake and the door looked like it was jumping right off its hinges with every thump. Eventually, as everyone nervously pretended not to look, backing up against the wall for fear of getting the same treatment as the door, one of the nurses opened the door a crack. He shouted in her face while gesturing towards his room, and then everything went a bit mad. I'm not sure what happened but two male nurses grabbed him by the arms and dragged him back to his room kicking while he screamed down the corridor. I don't know what happened to him after. I feel sorry for him, I find it hard enough expressing myself in here and I speak the same language.

Police came in the evening to search for drugs, but they only searched the men's rooms, which I thought was odd because there's definitely women in here on stuff other than their prescribed meds. I'm not sure what the police found but a new sign went up when they left saying that only next of kin are allowed in for visiting from now on; it must have something to do with non-prescribed drugs being smuggled in. It doesn't affect me, the only people I let in here are my mum and dad anyway.

Damien was almost hysterical when the police were here though and his stammer was much worse. He has PTSD from serving years in prison when he was nineteen and 'doing jobs' for the IRA. While they were going through the rooms in the men's side of the ward, he was shouting loudly about how you can't trust the peelers and that they're all corrupt. He was trying to get the men to stop the police from going into their rooms but nobody could be bothered. The searches really set him off, though, and the rest of the evening he was like a broken record talking about how 'the bastards' follow him wherever he goes. He said that a few months ago, before he was admitted here, he was in a bar. A man had followed him in and watched him from the corner. He was sure he was a spy working for the British army. He must be a bit paranoid – no wonder he was admitted soon after that – but I'm probably hard on him because I get irritated by him so quickly. He has had a really rough time and I'd probably be the same if I'd had to deal with half of what he has. He told me that when he was younger he watched two of his best friends and his girlfriend get blown up and shot in front of him during the height of the Troubles. He has their names tattooed in a tricolour on his arm.

Joy tried to go down to dinner with no pants. She had a top on and a long translucent scarf – like a sarong you'd wear on the beach, wrapped loosely around her waist with nothing underneath, not even knickers. Thankfully one of the nurses caught her before she got too far and marched her back to her room – which she wasn't happy about at all – to put on some pants and a pair of trousers. But by that time some of the men had seen her and I felt sick to my stomach at the thought of them seeing her bits because she's older than my granny and doesn't know any better. The nurse must have had to engage in some serious negotiations to get her changed in time to still make dinner because the next time I saw her she was heading towards the canteen wearing the sarong over her head like a veil.

Today has been a bit mad and I'm exhausted by everything that's gone on and it seems the madness isn't over because while

I'm brushing my teeth for bed I hear music coming up the corridor. It's one of the nurses, who loves himself, with a guitar. He's of the opinion he's gorgeous and flirts with Chloe when he thinks no one's looking. He's playing 'American Pie' but he's a bit shit and thankfully by the time I'm getting into bed and turning the lights off, one of the men shouts down the corridor telling him to 'shut up and fuck off'.

Day 21

Anger

I was woken this morning by lovely Alice arguing loudly with one of the nurses outside my door, which isn't like her at all. Apparently Brian, the new guy, was in and out of his room all night long making noise. He's in the room next to Alice because there aren't any free in the men's section. He even opened her door once thinking it was his, giving her the fright of her life. She must be seriously sleep-deprived because it takes a lot to get her flustered. She's usually so calm and gentle but I can tell she's really on edge this morning. She's telling the nurse my exact thoughts from when I first came here – although more eloquently than I could ever have put it – about how she is here to get better but the extreme needs of some patients are making her anxiety and mood ten times worse. I felt the same anger and panic when I was first exposed to John and Kathleen's constant screaming day and night sitting in my room crying and trying desperately to block out the howls and shrieks. I agree with Alice that the environment here is counterproductive to any sort of recovery, but at the same time – what can the nurses do? We are all here because we're sick and unfortunately there is no such thing as a loud ward for screamers and a quiet ward for those of us who need it. The nurse tells Alice she will do her best to keep Brian under control and away from her, and that last night was hopefully a one-off and won't happen again. Apparently he's moving out of the female section today and down to the men's. Someone there must be getting home.

Oh, God, the saddest, most heart-breaking thing ever has just happened and I'm trying not to cry. At breakfast Brian tried to apologise to me for making noise in the night. He was pointing to his ears and putting his hands together like he was praying. I could almost make out a few words he was saying although they were more like grunts. It looks like he has dentures too small for his mouth and not stuck down to his gums. He must have heard Alice complaining about him to the nurses earlier and maybe thought it was me. He kept trying to give me a pound coin from his pocket by way of an apology and tried to push it into my hands with his big grubby fingers. He was so sorry. I hate the thought of him being upset or feeling unwelcome or like he shouldn't be here. Even though he's more than double my age and I've only known him for a day, I think he needs protecting and looked after. He is sick, like everyone here, and I'm sure he's a good person.

The OT came to my room this morning to invite me to the driving range up the road with her and a few of the other patients who have out-of-grounds passes. It's something those with passes are allowed to do to get away from the hospital and engage with the outside world a little. I wouldn't have minded going – Chloe next door is and she's nice if a bit intimidating – but I said no. I could see the disappointment on the OT's face because we both know that I'm yet to join any group outings (which apparently the doctors like to see before discharge) but I don't admit that I wouldn't go for fear of people seeing me with the others and the nurses and guessing where we'd come from. I know the few who are allowed out and it's definitely a group that would make you look twice. The OT continues to talk about how I might enjoy it and that it could help my anxiety, but I'm imagining the normal people who might be there. I imagine them staring and pointing at us and thinking what a mismatched group we are and laughing at us and being scared to come anywhere near us. What if the people who work there have been told we're psychiatric in-patients and whisper behind our backs and take pictures of us and tell their friends? Even worse, what if I know someone there and had to speak to them and they saw me in my basically pyjama attire and then told everyone I know about the state I'm in? The OT stared at me, hoping she'd changed my mind but there's no way I can go now having catastrophised the whole situation in my head, so she leaves disappointed and I beat myself up for hours afterwards for letting her down.

I was talking to a boy called Martin today. He's around my age and he told me that this is his fourth time in one of these hospitals in less than two years. I used to find it crazy that people could be admitted more than once in their lifetime but since being here I can see it's unlikely anyone would recover here and so the need for multiple admissions is understandable. Imagine if people were actually helped the first time and didn't need to keep coming back? He has been here for six weeks this time and thinks he has at least another four to go. He looks big and tough and scary with thick black eyeliner and a long fringe covering one of his eyes. I imagine screaming heavy metal coming from the chunky headphones wrapped round his neck. He has dark purple bags under his eyes that make him look like he hasn't slept for weeks. Maybe he hasn't. But, like most people I eventually speak to in here, he isn't what I expected. He speaks quietly and gently and admits that he carries a notebook with him so he can write things down when it all gets too much, and through his headphones he listens to meditation CDs. He seems really smart.

He got a new jug of water and poured me a drink when I tried to pour from a jug I hadn't realised was already empty. I was a bit embarrassed and could feel myself going red. Martin hopes to get out of here by Christmas Eve – he has a room waiting with Dale in supported accommodation. They're going to be neighbours, just like in here, which is good. He said he didn't have any friends before but now he and Dale are really close, which is great. They can look out for each other because I've heard from Dale it can be a bit rough where he's going. I knew Dale didn't have any other option because he told me he was homeless, but I thought I'd seen Martin's sister come to visit before and I asked him if he had family he could live with. He said he has a mum and a sister and a stepdad but that 'home's a bad place'. His face darkened when he said it, so I didn't ask him anymore.

Dale joined us then and told me he's going to the zoo today because he wants to talk to the animals. I tried hard to keep a straight face because it's ridiculous, but he was deadly serious and told me he'd teach me how to do it when he gets back.

Dale isn't very friendly to many people in here, but he is to me. I think it's because one time he was out of papers for his roll-ups with no pass to go to the shop for a while and I asked Mum to bring him some. Also, maybe it's because he's met my dog a few times when he comes with Mum for a walk around the hospital grounds and Dale loves dogs. Dale comes and sits by me whenever I make it to the canteen and doesn't really talk to anyone else except me, Martin, Alice and Max. He carries crystals round with him and keeps offering to do reiki with me, whatever that is. He is totally different to anyone I've ever met outside here. Most of what he says is a bit strange but he's a hundred per cent confident and sure of himself – he would need to be with the attention he must get from his face tattoos, the swinging walking stick, the sunglasses and big-rimmed hat he wears no matter the time of day. He said something about us going for a walk with my pup when we get out of here because he's trying to surround himself with good people and the only people he knows on the outside are drug dealers and alcoholics. I'm such a bad person because my immediate thought was that I'd be too embarrassed to be seen with him – anxious with the thought of people staring at his unusual look and me by extension. Usually I prefer to fly under the radar. But I told him we could and he seemed happy.

Mum met Damien at the door when she was coming in during visiting hours. Of course he clung to her as someone new to speak to and talked at her the whole way down the corridor. I wouldn't care except that he continued the conversation until he was standing right inside my room. Thank God I was dressed and just sitting on the bed waiting for Mum to arrive. He stood by the bathroom while Mum took a seat and told us his whole life story. Mum felt sorry for him and encouraged him, asking questions which meant he stayed longer. I kept trying to catch Mum's eye to signal to her to be quiet so he might leave but she didn't notice. Finally, after twenty-five long minutes, I'd had enough. I said I was tired and got into bed and Damien reluctantly left.

When he was gone I shouted at Mum for letting him come into my room and keeping him talking. I was so angry. Mum was apologising but it was too late. I couldn't even look at her face because I knew she was distraught, which would make me feel even worse for lashing out. It wasn't her fault – Damien doesn't need an invitation, and really it's me who flies off the handle at the smallest things these days. She was desperate to stay for a while but I felt so embarrassed and annoyed at myself, and still mad at her a little, that I turned the lights off and told her to go. She left looking like she might cry, which broke my heart, but my head was shouting so much hatred at myself that I couldn't open my mouth to call her back or say I was sorry.

I'm alone in the dark now and still feel overwhelmed with anger. I'm livid at myself, at Mum, at Damien, at everyone and everything. There's that much rage inside me that if I wasn't so paralysed with exhaustion, I would flip my bed and smash the toilet seat and throw the chair against the wall. I feel angry about so many things that I can't pinpoint any single cause. What's stopping me from texting Mum to apologise is that I think some of this anger towards her has been building for years and years now, stemming from when I was little and felt let down and ignored. I've never addressed any of that or said it out loud so it's here, festering inside me. I feel such guilt from my behaviour and my words. I know I'm not meant to be this person. I flip my pillow to the dryer side (my tears have it soaked) and fall asleep to the repeated shouting in my head: 'I'm disgusting, everyone hates me, I don't deserve anyone's love'.

Day 22

Me versus Them

The doctor calls me to the conference room today and tells me I should start going home for a few hours each day because they're going to discharge me for good, probably within the next ten days. I'm in shock but I nod and agree and sign something. I can't believe it because it's come out of nowhere and I definitely wasn't expecting it or was prepared. I obviously knew I wouldn't be here forever, but I thought there would be some sort of treatment before I was sent home. There are two junior doctors in the meeting, the consultant, two nurses and someone I don't even know. I sit on one side of the table alone in my pyjamas so it's me versus the six of them and it's intimidating. I think maybe they've done it this way on purpose so I can't ask any questions or argue.

As soon as I'm back in the sanctuary of my room and get my breathing under control, I rack my brain for anything the doctors or nurses have done to help over the last three weeks. I wish I'd asked them that – or asked why they thought I was ready to be discharged home. Because nothing has happened – they've done nothing to try and understand why I'm sick or why things got so bad or what might help. What if this happens again?

It's later, when one of the younger OT girls comes to my room to invite me to make Christmas crafts, that I start to cry and it tumbles out that I don't think I'm prepared for discharge in a few days' time. I'm torn admitting this because on one hand it's horrible here; there's no way anyone could recover in this environment and I don't want to stay any longer. But on the other hand I came here with hope that I might be helped to get better. I tell her I came to hospital because I couldn't guarantee my safety and nothing has changed or been put in place to change that. Why am I being sent home again? I tell her I'm frightened and have too many feelings I can't cope with: sadness and guilt and shame and hatred and anger. They flood my brain and my body and I'm overwhelmed. The awful, dangerous thoughts explode back into my head like they did before and I know I'm not strong enough to ignore them forever. She tells me she could relay what I've just told her to the doctors, but I beg her not to. I'm afraid of Scary Doctor Lady and the way she twists my words and undercuts everything I say with medical jargon I don't understand. It's not fair. When I'm with her I feel I have to prove I'm sick and try to convince her I need help. I shouldn't have to do that. But I missed my chance to say no or question the decision this morning because I was in shock and intimidated and embarrassed – I hadn't even brushed my teeth when I was called out of the blue to go to the meeting room. I couldn't speak up for myself in front of all those people looking down on me.

My head is buzzing. I try to distract myself with a book and then a shower but I can't stop thinking about having to pack everything up and go home. It makes my chest hurt and my heart beat faster. My breathing is more difficult when I imagine it in my head. I don't get a say in where I go and when and what happens to me. I have to follow orders and hope the doctors know what they're doing, but I've lost all faith that they know anything about how to treat depression or mental illness. It's the same with most doctors I've ever met outside here too.

So far I've been mostly ignored and the only 'treatment' I've had is higher doses of medications when I've made it obvious I'm at breaking point. Why was I even brought here if this was all that would happen? What is the point of this? Why is it even called a hospital when no one is made better or helped? It's more like a prison – in fact, I bet some prisons are nicer than this. I begin crying and panicking at the thought of leaving and moving back home. I go to one of the nurses who gives me a diazepam and within fifteen minutes everything starts to blur and soften.

A few hours later, when I wake up and my words stop slurring and my brain feels not as sluggish, I find a nurse. I ask her if I can take diazepam home with me. She says no. Then I ask what I do if I get upset or stressed at home. Hearing it out loud we both realise how bad it is that in the last few weeks the only response I know to feeling panicked or anxious is a heavy-duty sleeping tablet. But the nurse tells me not to be scared of going home because the social worker I met yesterday – for less than ten minutes – said to her on the way out that she thought I was 'looking much better'. This is compared to the last time I saw her, about a week ago, and it seems the nurse has taken this as a sign I've somehow improved. The social worker spoke to me for a few minutes about who lives at home and whether they're at work, and because she came at a time I was awake and not under the influence of my meds she decided I'm better? She never asked me how I am or how I'm feeling. Why does her random assumption based off nothing carry any weight? It's inaccurate and unfair for her and then the nurses to decide how I'm feeling without consulting me. Not one of them has asked how I am. Surely *I'm* most likely to give them the best insight into *me*. Is that one fleeting comment from the social worker yesterday the reason I'm being sent home soon? I know I'm here for my mental state but that doesn't mean I'm unable to contribute or have a conversation about the next steps in my well-being and recovery. I feel like storming into the doctor's office, standing in front of her and screaming: 'I AM NOT BETTER. NOTHING HAS BEEN DONE TO HELP ME GET BETTER. NOTHING HAS CHANGED.' But, of course, in reality I do nothing.

I'm still racking my brain trying to think what has given the social worker the indication that I've improved. Maybe I'm missing something? All I can come up with is that I'd showered before she came and my hair was still damp. Maybe the previous time I saw her I looked like I hadn't washed in a while. Little does she know, it took absolutely everything I had yesterday to have that shower and I slept for hours after because it took so much out of me. I am at the bottom of the list of people to talk to about my mental state and well-being, yet I haven't had one moment of clarity or insight from anyone here about what's happening or what has happened to me. I haven't had one piece of advice on how to get better or be well. Surely that's not right? I can't be the only one who sees how non-existent the 'care' has been here.

I'm upset and deflated at this and annoyed at myself for ever thinking I could get better here or start to recover. And I'm annoyed at the social worker for deciding how I am without asking me, and the nurses for accepting her stupid comment, and the doctors for doing nothing but deciding to send me home with no good reason. I'm agitated and there's a tightness in my chest.

I haven't missed the irony of this either. When I first moved here I wanted out straight away – I wanted back home and this was the very last place I wanted to be. But I'm used to it now. Here is safe. I know how the day works and the routines and I feel more comfortable. If I really need to I can find someone to talk to and help get me through a wobble. It feels like a strange sort of holiday where, although I'm mostly confined to one room, there's no need to worry about meeting people or making plans or cooking meals or spending money or facing the outside world. I worry that when I go home I'll be so anxious I'll never leave the house. I can get peace here too. I can cry or sleep or stay quiet without Mum watching me and reading into everything I do and say, looking for evidence I'm falling apart. Being in charge of who can see me and when has been nice.

Day 23

Holding It In

I had to go to bed last night without a sleeping tablet for the first time in three weeks, at the doctor's request. She thinks I need to get used to not having one every night before I go home next week. I still have my anti-anxiety meds and they make me sleepy and I take a double dose of them at night, so it's not like I've to go cold turkey.

I don't know if it's because I'm usually high when getting over to sleep here, but last night seemed like the noisiest night ever. The usual loud patients were overly shouty and unsettled and everything annoyed me – the touch of my pyjamas on my skin to being too hot then too cold with my blankets. The pillow was uncomfortable and I was aware of the street light outside my window streaming through the thin curtain.

I hadn't realised until last night just how much the sleeping tablet was working the last few weeks. I was close to getting over at one point and could feel my whole body getting heavier when I was jolted awake by the nurse's torch shining right into my face when she was on her rounds before she slammed the little shutter on the door window closed again. I saw her there at least three or four times, checking every hour, and then must have fallen asleep around two or three.

I've slept through until 8 a.m. but now it's like my body is stuck under the covers. I'm lying in bed fighting with myself to get up and open the curtains. I feel so heavy. It's then that I remember something from long ago that hurts to think about and it's like a belt tightens around my heart. Usually with something this painful I immediately crash down the barricades to shut it out and save myself but right now I decide to let it in.

When I was younger, around eight or nine, I remember having tantrums like kids do where I would scream and stamp and shout and slam the door behind me and stomp up the stairs. Mum and dad would, what felt like, taunt me during these fits with names along the lines of 'drama queen', which was definitely true, but it hurt because, I suppose, at that age I didn't know how else to behave when I was angry or upset. Maybe if I was 17 or 18 and acted like that, it would be a fairer insult. It didn't take long, though, for me to decide that crying and shouting and showing emotion usually led to feeling mocked or embarrassed, and so I learnt to hold it in instead.

I still have that fear today. Even now, in hospital, I'm worried the doctors and nurses think I'm being dramatic, overreacting or looking for attention and they don't believe anything I'm saying. I find it difficult to ask anyone for help out of fear they'll shut me down or tell me I'm being stupid and over the top. I know that if I'd been more open with what was happening inside me, I wouldn't have imploded so drastically. I maybe felt I was protecting myself from ridicule or criticism by hiding everything behind a poker face, but the lasting effect is that I feel completely unable to show any emotion whatsoever in front of my family or those closest to me – sadness and tears or anger to even joy or laughter or happiness. I get ridiculously stressed or embarrassed at the prospect of crying at a movie in front of them or even telling them something funny that has happened.

That reaction and stupid comment from my family (and I'm crying now, of course) I think has done a lot of damage, but I don't blame my mum or dad or think badly of them at all. It's *me* who has taken things too much to heart and let throwaway comments eat away at me with dangerous consequences. I'm sure there's hundreds of times my family told me I was great and amazing, but I didn't hold on to any of those. I worry that the comments that haunt me run too deep to ever be removed. They've had so long to grow roots in me that surely it's impossible to undo the beliefs I have about myself. I've lived with the thoughts that I'm fat and ugly and a drama queen for as long as I can remember. I one hundred per cent believe these perceptions of myself, even if others tell me they're wrong.

To confront these, too, would take a level of communication with my family that I'm not capable of and I worry it would seem like I'm blaming people and worsen relationships further. I might open up painful wounds for other people that they've forgotten about. Imagine I shared any of this with my family and it made them feel guilty or upset. I can't put this onto anyone else and I don't want to take that risk.

The OTs have really been ramping up the activity timetable with different festive projects. It's only a few weeks to go until the big day and there have been Christmas crafts, a Christmas singsong (cringe), wreath-making and there's Christmas cookie-making happening later in the week. Some of the activities I wouldn't have minded going to and maybe even would have enjoyed but the thought of being around the other patients, having to make conversation and being watched by the staff while they make notes on my behaviour and how they think my mood is has stopped me from going. Also, I don't really want to do Christmas this year with the extra pressures to socialise that comes from everyone being home and off work and the stress and exhaustion of dealing with crowds of friends and family. The excessive food doesn't help either.

The good thing about these activities going on, though, is that it gets Damien away for an hour. He has to get involved in absolutely everything, so we get some peace and quiet for a while when he's away. One of the nurses was in a good mood and feeling in the Christmas spirit earlier. She asked one of the men in the dining hall if he was going to dress up as Santa to give presents out to the patients on Christmas Day. He replied that only if she would sit on his knee. Now everyone feels uncomfortable and no one knows where to look and everyone's trying to escape.

Day 24

The Need to be Heard

It's really heavy snow when I wake up this morning. I make my way round to the canteen for breakfast and I see Damien outside in his pyjamas making snow angels in the smoking area. I'm about to knock the window and tell him to come in before he catches a cold but then I remember he's thirty years older than me and if it's making him happy, great.

Damien is the neediest person I've ever met. He requires constant attention and validation all day long. His voice is loud and continuous. He never stops talking about himself and the things he's done. It's embarrassing and exhausting to be around. I wish I could be rude enough to ignore him like some of the others do. I had to admire over and over again while trying to eat breakfast the awful haircut he gave himself this morning. Then I had to look through the blurry images of the snow he had taken on his phone. And now, any time anyone comes near the Christmas tree, he stops them for a compliment because he decorated it 'all by himself'. Right now I can hear him from my room telling some long, dramatic and probably fake story to the nurse on special obs outside Kathleen's room. He won't leave them until they give him enough engagement and praise that he's sufficiently satisfied. On a better day I'd feel sorry for him, but today I need him to stay far away.

Mum is sending me videos and pictures of the puppy running and jumping about in the snow in our garden for the first time and he's loving it. Again, I get that guilty feeling – like a bad mother missing the fun times and milestones in my baby's life. I said this stupidly at breakfast in the canteen without thinking. Mark then said the same about his son who is experiencing snow for the first time too and he isn't there to enjoy it. I felt awful for comparing my dog to having a real baby and I could see on his face how much it pained him to be missing out yet again.

Today at lunch I was sitting beside Joy who was pouring almond milk into her tomato soup until it almost overflowed. She tried to get me to sing 'Amazing Grace' with her. I didn't want to disappoint, so I moved my lips silently while she belted it out at the top of her voice before one of the nurses told her to stop and eat instead. Afterwards she told me she had had angina in the night but the Lord came and saved her from it. She also told me off for drinking the juice on the table and told me to drink water instead because the devil puts toxins in juice.

I can hear a nurse outside my door booking a hair and make-up appointment for the staff Christmas night out that must be sometime next week. My friend group from university are trying to organise a Christmas night out for the eight of us but so far I've avoided saying what days I'll be free. I'm pretty sure I'll be out of hospital by the dates they're suggesting but I don't know what state I'll be in and I can't imagine making it on a night out. I feel like a fraud not being honest with them. Only one of the girls in the group knows I'm in here, while the rest think I'm still working in school like nothing's happened. My depression and anxiety aren't things I'd want to talk about over dinner and drinks and it isn't anything they'd want to hear about either. They're my friends, but I know that if I told them, they wouldn't know what to say and I worry they wouldn't act normally around me or they might see me differently. So often when you hear of someone in the news who's committed a crime or done something awful the tabloids attach a mental illness to them as if that's the reason they've done what they have. Which makes people start to believe that anyone with a mental health condition is potentially dangerous. So what if my friends found out and were nervous around me or afraid of me? If I did go I know I'd be quieter than normal and wouldn't be able to relax or enjoy myself. And I doubt I'd be allowed to drink on all the meds I'm on which might raise suspicion that something's up too.

I'm not strong enough or far enough away from any of this yet that I could talk about it in the past tense and say I'm better now and it's all behind me. Maybe when I can look back on this awful time from a better place I'll have the confidence to talk about what really went on and how sad it was. Maybe some day I could even help someone else going through the same awful time. What I've learnt is that you need people around you who you can trust to come back, no matter how many times you push them away or try to scare them off. People who will keep coming back, ready to listen and comfort and be there. Most of the time I don't need advice or want to hear about what worked for someone else. I just need someone to sit quietly and let me build up the courage to open up and admit how I'm feeling. I find it so difficult but I know it's necessary.

Of the very few friends who do know I'm here, in some ways I regret telling them because it becomes the elephant in the room. None of us know how to talk about it or what to say or how to bring it up. They want to ask me what's going on and why I'm in hospital and I want to tell them everything and be open and not afraid of how they'll react or be embarrassed that this has happened to me, but it feels too personal and vulnerable. It's like I'm standing naked in front of them telling them everything bad and painful I feel. Instead, I want to apologise quietly to everyone with my head bent in shame and embarrassment for existing and being such a burden. When they've asked me what's going on I've replied light-heartedly, 'Just having a little R&R', or 'Taking a break from school – it was mad!' I play everything down and hide the truth. I've always found it difficult to open up and be honest, but it's more because I'm trying to protect my friends from this blackness and awfulness and I don't want them to know how extreme things are, although I'm sure they must have figured it out, knowing I'm here. I've always seemed confident and happy and easy-going to them and I don't want to have to shatter that. I haven't accepted myself right now or this disease. How could I expect anyone else to?

The thing I don't understand, though, is how passionately I tell other patients not to be ashamed or embarrassed when they admit they feel the way I do. When they tell me they want to hide until they're fixed and enter back into the world as if nothing ever happened, I tell them – no! You have nothing to be ashamed of! You are brave and strong to be here and should be proud of yourself! And I mean it. I want them to own their illness and live in spite of it, yet if anyone on the outside was to ask me how work is or how I'm getting on or what I'm up to, I'm such a hypocrite. I know I'd lie and splutter and deflect and run away as quickly as possible. I can't admit to my depression. I guess no one likes to admit it when things are hard. But why do I care what everyone thinks of me? All my energy is given to interacting with people and keeping up this image and facade that I'm great! Everything's going really well! I'm having so much fun! It's exhausting and draining keeping up with the lies. I feel like life is bleeding me dry.

I realise in those moments how low I am when a 'Hello, how are you?' with someone passing by means I need bed for the next six hours, and those six hours are punctuated with the worst self-loathing and minute analysing of everything I said, how I responded, how I looked, whether they'll know what's happening inside or whether they'll see I'm hiding something. Could they tell I have depression? Were they thinking how fat I look today? Was I too eager? I imagine them off telling every other person they know about how strange and crazy and grotesque I am now. The thoughts become louder and I sleep another day away to make it through.

As another text comes through, still sorting out a date for the Christmas reunion, I think that maybe if I told my friends I'm in a psychiatric hospital, they might understand me not making it to the night out. They wouldn't ask any questions – it would let me off the hook, and it would save me having to lie about an ear infection or a tummy bug the day before to get out of it. Those excuses are short-term, easy fixed. Nobody feels awkward when someone says they have an ear infection. It's much easier to lie than admit there's something really wrong.

Oh, dear. Joy just came to see me to offer some almond milk (from the carton) or a sachet of jam she'd stolen from the canteen. She told me she'd tried to leave earlier because apparently the Lord has healed her now, but there were people 'opposing' her who wouldn't let her go. She told me she's going back to her room to pack her belongings and whispered to me conspiratorially, 'Sometimes you're better to not tell people and leave on your own,' three times in a row. Now I'm worried I should warn one of the nurses she's going to try and escape. I'll keep an ear out for her but knowing Joy, she'll have forgotten her plan and moved on to something else by bedtime.

Day 25

Body Dysmorphia

I can't for the life of me make a decision about anything today. I noticed it this morning at breakfast when the choice between Weetabix or toast took far too long and a line started to form behind me. It wasn't even that I was weighing up the calories or anything like that, I was staring and staring but my head was totally blank. It was like the bridges needed to form a response were missing and everything was still asleep up there. Then later the OT asked if I wanted to join the group that was about to start to make Christmas cards for family and friends. She must think I'm such a weirdo because after staring at her for what must have been almost a minute, I finally got out, 'No, thank you, not today'. When Mum called later to say the snow was still too deep for her to get out of the house and visit, I could barely answer her, and I imagined her on the other end of the phone thinking I'd been given a double dose of drugs today by accident, but I just couldn't muster up a response within a normal period of time. Has it always been this bad or have I just become aware of it? I'm going to lie down and see if sleep helps.

After my nap a woman I'd never seen before knocked on my door. She's some sort of counsellor – the nurse who promised to get someone to speak to me a few days ago asked her to come. She didn't really mention depression but we talked a little about my eating and bulimia but she said there wasn't much that could be done for either in here as it would need a more specialised approach. She thinks I have body dysmorphia because I hate so much about myself physically – everything about my appearance – and I pick myself apart and obsess over how disgusting and awful everything is. A tiny whisper of a question raises its head inside me: is she saying I'm not actually as repulsive as I think? But then I catch a glimpse of my outline in the mirror on the wall behind her and I smash that thought away again. Because if I was size eight with a symmetrical face, long, thick hair and smooth, glowing skin, I can see how it would be strange to think badly of myself. But I'm not. I know I'm fat and ugly and repellent.

Still, I can't stop thinking about the counsellor's body dysmorphia comment. I've nearly used up all my data googling it on my phone since she left. I think about my reflection. On days I'm feeling brave I can side-eye myself in the mirror, but when I do I recoil at what I see staring back in that quick glimpse. I feel hatred and anger and shame at my reflection. I react exactly how I should – how anyone would towards the vileness and ugliness, and because I'm too much of a wuss to get some sort of surgery, I need to try and forget how awful I look and that I will never be attractive. I know I need to get back on my diet when I get out of here too. I should have said to the counsellor that if she looked like me, she would hate it all too. It can't be dysmorphia when the bad stuff is accurate and true. Maybe if I was confident enough or felt good enough in other ways I could be braver and not obsess over the disappointment of my physical appearance. I can't massively change the way I look, but maybe if I could be one of those people who don't care what other people think, I wouldn't be so sad. How to do that, though?

I have had approximately two meals in here (not counting breakfast because you can't really get toast and cereal wrong). The lunches and dinners are revolting. I'd never considered myself to be a fussy eater before but I can't stomach the dirty, sloppy mush that's served up. The meals are still in their packaging from being unloaded off the van they're delivered in and they lie festering and writhing under the weird light that's meant to keep them warm but which doesn't do a good job. Nothing looks like it should and any of the ingredients are a total guess. It's the opposite of fresh or healthy and it all tastes the same too, which is unnerving. And the way it's dished up on grey plates that were once white with everything slopped on and dripping off the edges, served by people with hair hanging down and no gloves and no interest in their jobs or the people in front of them doesn't help. It's not their fault, I suppose – they're probably getting paid next to nothing. The smell, too, when you go anywhere near the kitchen is foul – lumpy gravy and grey chewy meat and sweaty mushy veg. I should be six stone coming out of here, which would be great, except that lucky/unlucky for me, Mum marches in every day, loud and confident as if none of this phases her, and leaves enough food to overflow the tabletop. If only so much of it wasn't wasted down the toilet after a binge.

She tries to hide her alarm at refilling my stocks each day and it makes me die inside. My stomach drops and I hold my breath tight in case she asks how I could have gotten through an entire packet of Kit Kats and a six pack of crisps in a few hours. I start to think of an excuse but she never asks so we both pretend not to notice and together we act like it's okay and normal and we ignore what it stands for. This time I really shout at myself and make myself promise I will be in control and not binge on all the food in one sitting and then hate myself and be sick and put on weight every day. But even as I'm thinking it I know it will happen.

From across the hall, Joy's hysterical laughter at nothing interrupts my thoughts and it's so creepy I'm glad the nurses are on a special outside the next room. If she tries to sneak in and exorcise me during the night, they might be able to stop her.

It's the new girl, Rachel, who's on special obs. She must be here because she attempted suicide. She came in last night and was put next door to Joy. Since she's arrived I've wished for a rule of quiet time from 11 p.m. to 8 a.m. or something because it's midnight now and with Rachel's door open for the nurse to see her, I've been listening to reruns of *The Simpsons* from across the corridor for hours now and can't sleep. She must have come prepared and downloaded every episode there's ever been before she was admitted. She has mainly been in her room but earlier when we were lining up for bedtime meds she was in front of me. I said 'hi', smiled and tried to be friendly because we must be around the same age and she didn't know anyone, but she stared at me for a minute and then turned around again. I shouldn't have bothered.

The snow has cleared enough now for Mum to get up the hill in the car to visit, which is good timing because I need to get outside and get some air and I have to wait for Mum to be with me. Mum brings me a scarf and hat and we walk around the other hospital buildings in the grounds for a while. At the start I feel exposed and jittery being out. I jump at everything and can't get my breathing steadied. I worry that someone I know will be driving through and see me, so I keep my head down and stare at the ground and I'm glad there's a thick layer of trees between us and the busy main road. Usually by the time we're heading back to the hospital, about fifteen or twenty minutes later, I've started to relax a little and can breathe in the fresh air again. Then it's time to get buzzed back in and say goodbye.

Day 26

Struggling to Breathe

I've been rocking back and forth on my bed for nearly an hour now and I can't stop. I'm trying to comfort myself and calm down with the repetitive motion but it's not working and I'm crying and struggling to breathe.

I can't stop thinking about the days leading up to being admitted, probably because I know I'm going home in a few days. Usually I'm angry and frustrated at myself when I think about how weak I've been, but now I feel sad for how ill I was (am?). Everything was painful and I was desperate to end it all. There was a constant screaming and hammering in my head all day long and it was a horrible way to live. I can see myself now, how exhausted and close to the edge I was. A breeze would have blown me over. It's the first time I've ever felt something like compassion for myself without blame.

I start to think, why didn't anyone help me? How did the people around me not know? But I remember doing everything to hide what I was feeling. I didn't let anyone see me or look at me because I knew it was written all over my face. I was head down, no eye contact – no contact at all if it could be avoided. I was terrified of anyone finding out how sick I was and then calling me crazy. And even if they had tried to help me, there's only so much anyone else can do. It had been at least three years before I finally told the nurse that day, crying, that I had a plan and knew what I was going to do. Psychiatric admission was the only thing I hadn't tried and I felt like I owed it to myself to try everything once before giving up for good.

It has hit me today that they're sending me home soon and I won't be better when they do. Like anyone, I thought that when you went to hospital the doctors and nurses fixed you and then sent you home. But now I know this won't be happening and I'm scared today for what I might do. I realise that no one has really mentioned what to do with my eating disorder – am I supposed to sort that out by myself? Do I need to do it alone? I'm left every day to sit on this little bed and try to keep busy and alive until occasionally a nurse or doctor remembers I'm here. Yet when they do come, they aren't listening and don't stay long enough for me to open up to them. I can see their minds are already on the next patient or their next duty or maybe what they're having for dinner later.

No one seems to care. No one knows how to make me better. They want me stable and looking more like I won't kill myself so they can strip my bed and make it up for the next patient in through the door. I'm just another number. Someone else to get in and out. These people can't help me, so what's the point of being here? Maybe I am better going home and trying to recover on my own.

Joy had visitors today. Her two daughters came and washed her hair for her in the shower, which she was excited about. She told everyone over and over again after they had left. She was so pleased she didn't even notice when people were blatantly ignoring her but then she never gets that anyway. Joy's room is right opposite mine and I heard one of her daughters step out into the corridor to take a call. She wandered over to outside my door to get out of earshot of Joy. She was complaining about her mother, saying how she was 'going on and on like a crazy rabbit' and that she'd been trying to leave for an hour but couldn't get away. I hope no one feels that way when they're visiting me. The daughters only come once a week for a little while at a time, but it makes Joy's whole day afterwards. I'm sad for Joy now. She's completely oblivious. She can be very tiring but it isn't her fault she's not well.

Rachel is again blasting loud, angry music from her room like an angsty teenager. She's still on special obs and the nurse is watching over her from outside. That nurse's head must be pounding. The walls are so old and thin here that even when Rachel's door is finally allowed to be closed, the noise will seem just as loud.

Alice told me she'd heard they're building a brand-new state-of-the-art psychiatric hospital in Belfast. It's going to be super high-tech, have TVs in every room and be ultra-modern and comfortable. It sounds great if it ever happens. We said it would be more like staying in a hotel than a hospital, which would be nice. But we both agreed that it wouldn't matter how nice the surroundings were if the care was just as crap. Money would be better spent on training and education for the staff instead, on implementing real changes that would actually help people rather than a fancy new building. Who are the people deciding how these hospitals are run? Have they ever struggled with mental illness? Have they had to spend time in hospital or try to recover? I would guess not. From nearly a month of being between the two hospitals and speaking to the patients, I have a list of about fifty things I can think of off the top of my head that would help the patients in here, and none are expensive or difficult or particularly mind-blowing. It's simple common sense stuff that would increase the likelihood of people getting better and not having to return after being discharged. Maybe I'll write a letter to Stormont when I'm out.

I am fighting really, really hard today against a bad little voice getting louder and louder, shouting at me that I'll never get better, I'm useless and ugly and stupid and I should die now and do the world a favour. I promise myself that if a nurse comes to see me today, I'll tell them. But no one comes all day and I cry myself to sleep at night.

Day 27

Structure

Ifeel torn right now and it's making me anxious and on edge. I've been left back to hospital after a few hours out with Mum, Dad and the puppy. We took the pup for a walk in the last of the snow until I got tired and then went back home and had dinner. I'll be leaving in a few days' time I think, which is why I had such a long trip out today that included going home for a while, but I'm terrified. Being under my parents' constant watch and feeling their tension and fear from not knowing what to do or say to me is a pressure I never meant to burden any of us with. They tiptoe around me and I hate it. They've had the same amount of guidance and support as I have had over the last month: none.

It's a sad reminder as we drive back to hospital that I'm not normal and this is where I need to be right now because I'm still sick. But there's a sense of relief too. I'm safe here and there's a peace in knowing there's nothing I need to do and I have no responsibilities or pressures. Maybe this is why I'm here – for a break rather than to get better and fixed, like I thought. I can escape to my room and for the most part I'll be left alone. This safe little cocoon can be warm and familiar. All I have to do is (sometimes) dress myself, and the farthest I ever have to go is the canteen if I can be bothered. It's always a great success when I make it the whole way there and back without meeting anyone or having to talk, but even when I have to stop and speak to someone, no one judges what state I'm in. I haven't worn make-up or anything other than pyjamas or tracksuit bottoms for four weeks now. My face can be red and tear-stained and blotchy and no one here minds or is scared. The patients are the few people who instinctively know when to talk, when to listen and when to just sit and be there. It's a great skill to have.

I know that after a few weeks at home I'll need to venture out of the house and see people other than my mum and dad. Then what – getting properly dressed and into the car and putting on an act that I'm good and well for everyone else's benefit? The thought of the smiling and the pleasantries and answering the 'What have you been up to?' and 'How's work?' questions makes me want to close the curtains and stay in bed forever. I don't know how else to *be* outside if I'm not pretending.

My days in here are structured around mealtimes, medication rounds and visiting hours. I can't remember how to fill a day at home – not in a positive way anyway. I asked a nurse who said I need to have a good routine set up for when I get out of hospital because it's been a month in this sheltered environment and it will be a hard transition. I'm scared. I remember the weeks leading up to hospital and I couldn't get out of the house most days, and if I did, bad things happened, like driving to places to cry and planning how to hurt myself. What will stop me from getting back into that pattern again? I can't be sure that anything inside me has changed.

I've grown attached to this horrible place and although I dislike it I know when I'm free and think back to my days spent hiding here I will miss the space it gave me to think and the room it gave me to breathe. Maybe the doctor is right – it is time to go. Too much longer and I'll become too dependent on this place and more fearful than I already am of the outside world. It will be hard to readjust to life when I feel so affected by this experience – a little bit traumatised but a little bit enlightened too. Will I act differently? Will I ever tell anyone? What will they think of me if I do?

The new man, Brian, has the same name as my dad and must be around the same age. He's difficult to understand when he speaks but he's still determined to talk to everyone. The staff are quite harsh with him – always telling him to sit down, finish eating and stop talking to people in the canteen, when he doesn't seem to be doing any harm. He does get distracted at mealtimes, though, because he wants to shake everyone's hand and some people don't appreciate it, which is fair enough. Whatever handover notes the staff here got must have told them to be strict with him because you can tell he's used to it. When the nurses scold him he does exactly what they say straight away, like a child. It breaks my heart to see. Is he somebody's daddy?

You can always tell quickly with the patients and the staff whether they are approachable or not, and I know straight away that Brian is a good, kind man. He continuously offers out one of the cigarettes he keeps tucked behind his ears and smiles at everyone with his big gummy mouth. But then at dinner I see why the nurses have to be all over him. Like a switch being flipped, he is standing over a patient who took the salt from him. His whole face and body changes in a way that makes him seem big and scary with the potential to hurt someone. The nurses come then and shout at him and push him down into his seat. They moved the salt user to another table.

The same thing has happened a few more times now where Brian will be eating at the table then suddenly jump up and start shouting, or he'll be walking in the corridor and then turn and get right into the face of the nurse who's trailing him and shout nonsense at them. I don't think he means what he's doing, though, because within a few seconds he is calm and sweet and smiley again. There must be such a spectrum of disorders in here.

I'm almost asleep, right on the edge about to tip over, when a torch beam shines into my face and startles me and I jump up in a panic. I squint to see one of the nurses on her night check bang the shutter on the door window before moving on to the next room. Even with that familiar nightly routine, it still takes a few seconds to remember where I am.

Day 28

Forty Years Ago

I tried to tell Mum today that I don't want to do Christmas this year. In reality I want to pretend it isn't happening at all but I downplayed the strength of my feelings because she likes Christmas. I brought it up by saying that maybe we shouldn't bother with a Christmas tree because the puppy might try and pull it down, and reminded her that she complains every year about the nuisance of getting the tree up and down, but she said not to worry, that she'll get it up this weekend and keep an eye when the puppy's around it.

She thinks I'm trying to be kind by telling her not to worry about it but it's selfish on my part. The thought of seeing all the family and opening presents in front of people and sitting opposite each other making conversation, eating a meal, feels too much. Food is the thing stressing me out the most, though, because I know what will happen: the typical Christmas overindulgence that I won't be able to stop obsessing over and then time spent trying to find ways to sneak off to the toilet alone or drive to an abandoned park with a plastic bag. I wish I could've gone to sleep on the first of December and wake up after new year.

I know I wasn't clear enough with Mum when she later sends me pictures of the decorations down from the attic for her to get started constructing the tree. I know she's trying to include me but I don't care for any of it. God, I am horrible.

I need to make it clear for myself that I don't blame my mum and dad for any of this. They are such good people who were faced with some shitty events. Maybe I wouldn't have dealt with them like they did, but that's so easy to say in hindsight. There are thousands of people who have gone through so much worse – real traumatic, devastating life events, so I know it's *me* and *my* insecurities, and that I've let little things eat away at me for a long time. My parents have tried really hard in the last few years and given me such a wide berth when I've been incredibly difficult to be around. In the last few weeks, working through this stuff in my head and writing it down, I'm beginning to understand everything that's happened and I forgive them. I hope they can forgive me too. I know they only ever did what they could and what they thought was best. Even if they had done things differently, I would probably have ended up here anyway. It is me, and only me, who has put myself here. I'm the one who has allowed things to get to this extreme. And now I've realised that, sadly, it's only actually me who can make myself better again. My run-ins with doctors and nurses and therapists have made it clear that no one really knows what to do or say or prescribe. It's a difficult realisation after putting my faith for so long in those I was sure would 'cure' me. And although right now I'm just trying to survive each day, maybe soon I'll be strong enough to get myself onto the path of recovery.

Damien's marching up and down the hall singing The Pogues at the top of his voice and it makes me shudder. I unexpectedly remember how two Christmases ago, when I was feeling bad, my granny rang my mum and told her to tell me I hadn't to come to hers for Christmas Day if I didn't want to like we usually would. I don't think this option had even entered mine or my mum's head but my granny understood. She'd been there before and knew just what to say and do. Forty years ago she was here, in one of the buildings on this same site. She wasn't like me, though – she had a real reason to be admitted. She had just turned thirty and suddenly became a widow with five young kids in West Belfast at the height of the Troubles.

Granny would have been amazing to talk to about being here. She is the only person I know who has been in a similar situation. I remember a story she told me from the time she was in the hospital that always makes me laugh. Herself and the other patients had been warned to be on their best behaviour because there were some fancy VIP doctors coming that day to look around the ward. When they arrived, granny said that they wouldn't look at any of the patients and didn't want to get too close to any of them so herself and a few of her friends started walking towards them like zombies with their arms outstretched and making groaning noises to freak them out. That rebellious streak was her all over.

She knew I was struggling the last few years. I have a text saved on my phone where she called me a brave soldier and told me I would get better. She died a few months ago from cancer. This will be the first Christmas without her and the first Christmas I want more than ever to talk to her. Without sounding too crazy, I feel her here with me sometimes. When I'm at my worst and unreachable to anyone else, I talk to her and ask her to stay with me while I try and fight through what's going on. I know she wants me to stick around. I wish I could tell her how anxious and overwhelmed I am. Did she feel the same? I only ever knew her full of life – she recovered years before I was born. How did she do it? How did she come back from the brink and turn her whole life around? And why did I never ask her any of this when I had the chance? When I feel ashamed for being here I know she would tell me off and say she's proud of me for not giving up and for getting help. If she did it, maybe I can too. We are made of the same stuff, after all.

I wish I could be as strong as her. I know she would say I've been strong for too long. Ah, I'm crying now trying to imagine her here with me. But it's not bad, painful tears; I think it might be good tears, useful. Maybe these tears will help me heal.

Day 29

A Glimmer of Goodness

At breakfast there were nine or ten men scattered around the tables eating, and me. I don't know where any of the girls were. One of the men was talking loudly about his ankles swelling up in the night because of his medication, and then, HORROR!, another man made a joke about his penis doing the same. Thank God, I'd already finished eating and could scrape my dishes together loudly and make a big fuss of putting my bowl and cup away like I hadn't heard. But while I was trying to make myself invisible and leave as quickly as possible, Damien made things worse by having a go at penis-joke man for talking like that in front of a girl (me!) and one of the nurses had to step in and get him to sit down again.

Also at breakfast there was a man sitting beside me whom I hadn't seen before. He walked with a limp and I thought he must be new until he stood up suddenly, spilling his Rice Krispies, and began shouting nonsense into the empty space so loudly and violently that he had to lean on the wall behind him to hold himself up. I jumped about a foot in the air before I instantly recognised the shouts and knew he must be John who shouts and screams me to sleep every night from next door. He must be doing well if he's allowed into the canteen for a meal because for the nearly three weeks I've been here he's always had a tray of food brought to his room.

I presumed he was bedridden. Two nurses shuffled him out of the room after his outburst, one on each side, while he continued to shout and thrash about. The nurses called back to 'give him a wide berth' before anyone else decided to leave.

Another man took John's empty space. As he reached for the butter and jam in the middle of the table I saw the worst scars I've ever seen: thick and white and raised. They were all over the inside of his arm. There were two wide scars that sat above each of the veins in his wrist. I couldn't look at them without imagining the blood that must have gushed out. Thank goodness none of the scars seemed too recent – they were all healed over, but there must have been about thirty or forty covering that one arm alone. I looked closer at his face while he busied himself with his toast and thought about how I had misjudged this eccentric-looking man earlier when he'd sat beside me with his long white beard and crazy unkempt eyebrows. He is the same as me: sad and hurting and hoping to get better.

I was out for a few hours today with Mum and the puppy. We went for a walk around the hospital grounds and I continued trying to readjust myself to being in the real world. When I came back Damien was dying to fill me in on the drama I'd missed. Apparently one of the girls saw a bag full of bras hanging out of Brian's room (his door always has to be wide open). When the nurses investigated, sure enough, they found a bag bursting with women's bras and pants. When they questioned Brian on it he quite happily told them he'd stolen them from the last ward he was on. He saw nothing wrong with the sizeable stash he'd now accumulated. What was he thinking! The knickers are being taxied back to Brian's last hospital to try and find their owners. They probably should put them through the wash first.

Brian sits next to me a lot when I make it to the canteen for a meal. I've noticed he's a constant mover – he has this thing where he needs to always be doing something, sort of like he's tidying but actually he's mixing things up. In the canteen it's always the place mats or the cups or the sugar packets. In the corridors he's constantly dragging chairs about from place to place, taking them from somewhere and leaving them somewhere else. I didn't think he was aware he does it, but when I saw him fussing about earlier with magazines in the TV room I realised that he thinks he's helping. It's so pure and innocent on his part but I can see it's driving the nurses a bit mad.

Getting into bed just now I noticed two things and I'm writing them down quickly before the anxiety tablets kick in and make me drowsy. The first thing I noticed was when I was tying my hair up for bed at the mirror – I looked myself right in the eyes. Usually I focus on getting my hair in the scrunchie, but tonight, without planning to, I looked right at myself, at my whole face, for a few long, slow seconds. I can't remember the last time that happened. Usually I'm careful to only focus on whatever tiny part of myself I need to give attention to – one small section at a time, like an eyebrow or an eye or a lip. I avoid my reflection except when necessary and approach it slowly and with care, avoiding the whole picture and eye contact. It's normally too distressing to see the whole image at once, when it's uncontrolled. It overwhelms me and I feel burned by it and need to look away and distract myself. Tonight it was an accidental look for a second or two but it was actually okay. It wasn't as awful as the picture I've built in my head. I've let my thoughts about myself warp the image I have so that now I expect to see a huge, terrifying monster staring back at me and I swear that's not even an exaggeration. I truly believe that's what I look like because that's what I've been telling myself for so long. But that didn't happen.

The second shock came right after – I was climbing into bed and saw a tissue packet on the table beside the pillow and realised it hadn't been used all day. Oh, God. Something timid and tiny wakes up deep inside me because I know these must both be good things but I'm too afraid of admitting it and scaring them off. I can't allow myself to let any hope in or enjoy a whisper of celebration for even a second. This is too new, too delicate. I go to bed trying not to move in case the little glimmer of goodness that has hatched inside me gets frightened off and disappears. I pray silently into myself; please, please, please, let tomorrow be an okay day.

Day 30

Seeing the Future?

This morning at breakfast some of the others were talking excitedly about Taylor – a tall, skinny boy of 19 or 20 who ran off and went missing last night. (I've never been near him because he scares me.) Apparently at around 10 p.m. yesterday evening, when most of the corridor lights get turned off for bed, he went outside for a smoke, climbed over the big wire fence and ran off. One of the staff heard something and did a whip round to check who had gone. There's only about 20 of us in here, so it didn't take long for them to realise it was Taylor. They rang his phone and strangely enough he answered, said that he was meeting someone for a drink and would be back in a few hours. I think he expected the nurses to say that was okay and to go and enjoy himself, but they told him he needed to come back right away, so he hung up and stopped answering. The nurses rang his mum who tracked his phone and dragged him back to the hospital by his ear before midnight.

Everyone was still talking about it when he walked into the breakfast room this morning to whoops and whistles from the patients. He went bright red. Chloe and a few of his friends were congratulating him and asking him where he went and how many drinks he got in before his mum showed up. They were slapping him on the back, applauding him for his hour of freedom and I saw him smile for the first time, relishing the attention. Chloe and the boys around him don't ever get out. No one comes to see them or sign them out. They were happy to live through him and his adventure for a while.

The doctor stops by for a minute today and asks what I see for my future but I'm groggy and tired and can't answer. I continue to stare at her blankly, so she then tries asking specific questions that only require a yes or no answer: do I want to get married? Will I have children? I can't help but get annoyed at her questions. Would she ask men the same questions about marriage and babies? What about having a career or a life of my own? Why do I need to be married and have children to be happy or fulfilled? I'm not sure why she's asking, so I don't give any concrete answers and instead reply vaguely saying that I don't know, which is partly true, but I don't tell her I'm pretty sure I don't want children. I know she'd be surprised because I'm a teacher and should probably like kids. I also know she'll press me for why not, and I know that one of the reasons she'd find interesting is that I'm afraid he or she would inherit my genes and my mental health. I know part of my depression is hereditary – the doctors have told me as much, and I could never allow the chance of passing that on to someone else. I couldn't bear being even partly responsible for anyone experiencing what I have. I've seen and felt the anguish of my mum watching her child suffer and feeling powerless to help. I know I couldn't cope with that. I also worry what would happen if I went through another rough time like right now in the future. What would I do with a child then? I know from experience you can't hide things like that from children – that there's always some hurt or trauma left behind, but luckily all I have waiting at home is a puppy. Thinking about this baby stuff makes me wonder if I'd be allowed to foster or adopt because I've been in here. Does this rule you out of stuff like that? Oh, God, is this on my record forever? Can people see it? If I go for a new job, will my employers know? My thoughts start to get tangled, so I lie down, and when I open my eyes again it's dinner time.

At dinner I remember that lovely, gentle Alice has left again. I think it's for good this time. I saw her dressed for the outside world earlier with make-up on and her hair done, and although she looked so pretty, the bones jutting out angrily from beneath her baggy clothes and her teeny-tiny skeletal frame was a shock. She still looks so ill. I really hope Alice will be okay, but I wasn't feeling good earlier after the doctor's interrogation, so selfishly I didn't even go and say goodbye to her. This is the second time she's been discharged and tried to go home in the last week. The last time her room was left open for her in case she needed to come back, and she did return a few hours after leaving, but this time they haven't given her that option and they've already moved another lady into her room.

The lady in Alice's room has been shouting loudly ever since she got here – not in anger, more like she doesn't know how to stop. The whole ward heard the staff fighting with her because they couldn't get her arm to take bloods. The first few hours and days are daunting and distressing, so I'm giving her the benefit of the doubt – maybe she just needs time to settle. I hope she isn't going to be another John or Kathleen shouting through the night. I'm still getting used to falling asleep without a tablet.

An hour later and it seems the new lady has settled in, not because she's simmered – she's gone the other way and isn't shy at all anymore. Swearing doesn't bother me but even I'm embarrassed by some of the language the new lady is screaming over the ward. Everyone's a dirty c-word and an effing wanker. It's awkward but funny at the same time. I don't know how the nurses keep their cool sometimes.

I thought I might have got word I was going home today because the doctor had said it would be sometime this week, but she didn't mention it earlier and it's past six so she'll be away home for the night. The doctor needs to speak to me before she can okay the discharge, so I relax a little, knowing I won't be going anywhere tonight. I'm still torn between whether I'm feeling good about this or not. I have been feeling slightly better, not really thinking about hurting myself, but it always feels like another attack is just around the corner and I'm on edge waiting for it. I feel so anxious when I think about leaving but I've wanted out since I moved here. I know there's nothing happening tonight anyway. I'll worry about it again tomorrow.

Day 31

Light at the End of the Tunnel

Oh, God, it's loud and stressful today – maybe one of the worst I've experienced in a month on either ward. New lady's swearing and shouting adds to the daily howling competition between Kathleen and John. If it wasn't so hectic, I might find it funny because she was shouting off about Brexit earlier and calling Arlene Foster a slag. Kathleen, maybe sensing the tension new lady has brought in, is extra unsettled today too. Her torturous howling has been constant and piercing from seven o'clock this morning. It makes it worse that I've never seen her, just heard her screams throughout the day and night and heard her horrific story from the other patients. In my head she's like a banshee that haunts the ward, not really existing like the rest of us.

As if this day wasn't already difficult enough, Scary Doctor Lady stormed into my room to tell me I can be discharged today. I've to wait for home treatment to talk to me because they'll be the ones taking over my treatment on the outside and they need to arrange when they'll come out to the house, but I can start packing my stuff. She says it should be easier to get set up with long-term help from them than it was here because it's a smaller, more focused team. She finishes her sell by saying it's good I'm going today because 'the ward keeps getting worse'. She's right, but it doesn't make me feel better. I don't know if I'm ready. Is it the time to go? I know this isn't the end, and like the nurses keep telling me, no one goes home from here totally recovered – just over the crisis they came in on. And it's true, I'm not at the same point of distress that I was in four weeks ago. But going home to everyone and everything again after being in this safe little bubble for a month feels overwhelming.

I'm having a soft, quiet cry to myself, letting it sink in. I'm concentrating hard on breathing and making an effort not to panic. I try to take in the solitude and the privacy and quiet of my room. This room that has been a haven at times and a prison cell at others. But it stands for, hopefully, the beginning of my slow and painful recovery. I start to pack my things and realise that what I'm most scared of is that it feels like not enough has changed. Am I different now than when I first came to hospital? Can I trust myself? I'm worried that everyone will think that by leaving here I'm better and not sick anymore and they'll expect too much of me.

I've packed up my room – it didn't take long – and I'm perched on the plastic chair in the corner. (It doesn't feel right to sit on the bed anymore.) I try to imagine myself back home. I can't really get a good picture of it in my head. I know I'm being given another chance to start over, but that makes me sweat because I don't know how. It seems like such a big thing – where do I start? One of the nurses comes to check on me and in a panic I blurt out louder than I meant to that I don't know what to do when I get home. She tells me I need to structure my days minute by minute to get through the first week, from the second I wake up until I go to bed. Oh, God, it sounds exhausting. Structure it with what? So much to think about and my brain doesn't work at the speed it used to.

I can't deal with saying goodbye to people. I tried hard not to get too close to anyone while I was here because I always knew I'd eventually leave and I thought that when I did I'd want to draw a line under the whole experience, never mention it again and pretend none of it ever happened. But now that it's about to be over, I feel the opposite. I don't

want to forget I was here or that I needed this. I don't want
to forget the people I've met and the effect they've had on
me. I hope I've become a more tolerant person and wouldn't
be as quick to judge people as I was. I'm ashamed of myself
that when I was first admitted I felt I was better than the rest
of the people here. I thought they were scary and mad and
I avoided speaking to anyone for the first week or two. But
now they've become my friends. I go to Dale or Max or lovely
Alice when she was here and they know right away if it's a bad
day. They know what to say and how to comfort me. They
know when I need to sit beside them in silence and they pat
my back quietly if I cry over breakfast. I've felt closer to these
strangers in the past few weeks than anyone I've ever known
in my life. I've learnt so much from them and they've done
more for me than any nurse or doctor or tablet. They've taught
me what it is to open up and that, actually, I'm not alone in
this and I shouldn't isolate myself like I do. There's nothing
that they've said about how they're feeling that I haven't felt
myself. They've shown me that everyone struggles, and each
time I told them not to be ashamed and embarrassed of their
illness, I started to believe it for myself. I realise, too, from
being with these people, how lucky I am. Some of my friends
here have no family or no one in the world they can turn to
or lean on. Some people have no home to go to when they get
discharged, which makes me think, what the hell am I worried
about going home to my big comfortable house?

The people I've met here, they've become such a huge part of
my day, people I would never have had the chance to meet on the
outside world. What will happen to them? A few will probably
never leave, not that they know that, and that makes me want to
cry and take them with me. Everyone should have the chance to
be happy and live a full life. It sounds cheesy but maybe I can do it
not just for me but for Joy and Avril and even Damien.

Before, the thought of anyone other than my mum knowing
I was ill and in hospital was enough to send me into a full-blown
panic and under the covers for weeks at a time, but now I feel

some of the fight coming back into me. I was as close as a person could be to the edge, but very slowly and without me even knowing how exactly, I think I'm getting better and I should be proud of myself for that. Although right at this minute I don't feel it, I know that in the future I'll be stronger because of this whole experience. I never thought I would be twenty-four and leaving a psychiatric hospital, but it has happened, and I'll do everything I can to make sure it doesn't happen again.

I can't help but get wobbly and emotional waiting for Mum to come and take me home. I can see myself in this room crying and pacing and angry and sad and sorry over the past few weeks and it's like I'm watching someone else. For the first time I realise I didn't do anything bad to deserve being here. Wow. I'll write that again. I didn't *do* anything to deserve being here. It's a new and strange realisation and my eyes water again. It's tough to be kind to myself.

Now I hear the words a nurse said earlier: 'It's the time to be selfish'. I can't waste my energy on keeping up a fake front for other people to pretend I'm okay when I'm not. I spend so much time worrying about what everyone else thinks of me and how I come across, it's exhausting and unfair too. Right now I want to rid myself of the shame and embarrassment I feel from being here and living this. I want to scream and shout and be loud and strong for once and tell everybody that I was here. I want to tell everyone I know that I was sick and had to get help and there's nothing wrong with that. I know there will be bad days, but I've got through them before and I can do it again. I repeat that a few times and hope that one day I can really believe it.

Four weeks ago I honestly don't know what would have happened if I hadn't been admitted. I can't help but think I wouldn't be here when I remember how bad things were. I know now that I didn't want to die, I just wanted to end the pain and torture. I didn't know any other way to make that happen. I should be grateful I'm still here no matter how fragile and vulnerable I feel. I'm still sad and afraid and broken, but I suppose at least I'm feeling. A tiny voice, barely audible, comes from somewhere deep down and whispers, 'I can do this. I will beat this', and I hope with every single fibre in my whole body that it's true. It makes me feel like I've accomplished something when really I haven't done anything at all.

Mum is here now looking as nervous as I feel, so I need to dry my eyes, take a deep breath and imagine having a stomach of steel before leaving. The staff hug me and say goodbye and good luck, and I can't help it when my eyes flood again. I try to hide it but they see and pat my arm and tell me quietly that it will be okay, I will be okay and to take it one day at a time. The patients are gathered round too. They hug me and wish me luck and tell me they better not see me here ever again, which makes me laugh. It feels like I'm saying goodbye to a big extended family. I know they sense my apprehension and fear and I'm grateful for the millionth time of their presence here, but I can't put it into words to thank them. I hope they know. It takes a minute before I can move towards the door and I fuss with my bags. Then I think only about my feet and move them one step in front of the other. I can do this. They buzz me out for the last time and I don't look back even though I feel the eyes of the patients and the staff on me as I leave.

Deep breaths, here we go.

Finding Peace

I never planned on letting anyone read my diary from the most difficult period of my life. It was only recently I came across it and reread it myself from start to finish. I was amazed at the mindset I was in at the time because thankfully I'm so far from it now, five years later. As I read everything back and realised how ill I'd been, it was a stark reminder of how lucky I am to be able to say that this story has a happy ending.

Coming out of hospital was difficult and is a blur now (unfortunately I didn't continue to write things down). There were daily phone calls or home visits from the psychiatric support team for the first fortnight, but just like the team pre-hospital, these were no more than suicide check-ins and it was a different person each day. After this, a combination of finally being on medication that worked for my body and being assigned a consistent mental health nurse to meet with a few times a week got me through Christmas and new year.

I had felt a small shift in the days leading up to discharge and knew I needed to do absolutely everything I could to make sure I never needed to be admitted again. I was told the referrals for therapy could take a year, so in January I sought out help for myself. I understand how lucky I am to have had the support of my family and the time to do this.

One of the first organisations I found was AWARE. The first time I attempted to attend one of their support groups I couldn't get myself through the door, but the next week I got closer, and by the third week I managed to take a seat. This support group became a huge part of my recovery. I didn't speak for the first few weeks, just listened. It reminded me of being back with the patients in hospital. Everyone was so open, welcoming and supportive. It felt safe and I began to contribute to discussions and started opening up. I began to see everything that depression had told me about myself and everything it had taken from me reflected in the people in group. It made it easier to appreciate that this was an illness that had happened to me, just as it had all these other people, and that it wasn't my fault I had become sick. I felt so much empathy for the people around me that eventually I started to question why I couldn't allow myself any of that compassion, so for every kind thing I thought about another person I started to tell myself it too. Each week it got easier and I started to feel stronger. I even started giving other people advice and I looked forward to the groups each week.

At one of the sessions the coordinator approached me and said they'd been offered the services of a volunteer therapist from Queen's University and she wanted to put me forward. I began a new course of CBT with this doctor soon after and over the next few months started to understand the anxiety and panic I experienced. I had to let go of worrying about if he thought I was a nice person or if I was disappointing him and be honest. He helped me gain the confidence to start venturing out of the house and the panic attacks became less frequent. I was cautiously able to go back to things I used to enjoy, like meeting a friend for a walk or a coffee, knowing that if I felt anxious, I had strategies to overcome it. The biggest lesson I learnt was to stop running from situations that scared me and instead see them through. It was never as bad as my mind told me it would be.

Then I signed up to take part in every course I could find. Not only did I want to know everything I could, but it helped fill and structure my days. I attended AWARE's Living Life to the Full, Mood Matters and Mental Health First Aid courses. I remember crying silently in the first Living Life to the Full session when they played the YouTube video of the black dog because it was my experience with depression, explained so simply and without shame. My nurse signed me up to mindfulness and stress management classes run by local groups in Belfast. I contacted another charity, Lighthouse, and received counselling and relaxation therapy. My councillor in Lighthouse helped me see how my internal beliefs about my lack of worth and constant need to please everybody else was having a detrimental effect on my recovery. He also helped me to set goals to work towards for the future. Mum had also been able to contact a local charity, Cause, who support those caring for people with mental illness so she could finally get some information and support too.

I found some great podcasts to listen to about my eating disorder and started to look forward to taking the pup out for a walk every day to listen to the next one. I joined the Belfast Recovery College to learn more about how mental illness develops and is maintained and how to build resilience. I was armed with so much knowledge and finally began to understand what had happened in my brain. I started to put into practice some of the things I had learned, and even now when I'm having a more difficult day I go back to some of the material I kept from that time, reminding myself how I can help make things better. The easiest I find to implement is planning three things in my day, one that will make me feel I've achieved or accomplished something, one that will help me feel enjoyment and one that will allow me to feel connection. It could be as simple as making my bed, going for a walk and making dinner with my boyfriend.

After a few months I was referred for Interpersonal Therapy by my GP, which I found life-changing. My therapist was patient and every week gave me tasks and reading to do outside our sessions. She taught me how to lean on the people around me when I needed help and supported me in making peace with the past. One of the hardest but most liberating things she encouraged me to do was speak to my family about the things that had haunted me for years. Although it was far from easy, I felt a weight lifted from my shoulders and I was able to appreciate events from my mum's point of view and let go of the anger and hurt I had carried for so long.

When IPT finished I was referred to the Eating Disorder Services for CBT. I had been referred there years before where the first thing that was said to me was, 'We're not going to talk to you about sticking your fingers down your throat because we know you're the expert on that', and then I was put into a room on my own every week for 8 weeks to click through an online course on bulimia. The message I took from them that time was that I wasn't sick enough to deserve any real treatment or help. Which is a dangerous spark to light in the mind of someone with the competitive and manipulative illness of an eating disorder. So I didn't hold out much hope when I was referred back there again. But it definitely felt like they took me more seriously this time around and although I can't be sure, the only difference since the last time was that I was in a starvation period of my bulimia at my assessment and so I had lost a significant amount of weight in a short period of time. This seemed to be enough to offer me eating-specific CBT. And although I was grateful that this was being offered now, it did make me sad that years before when my bulimia was just as bad, because I didn't measure as underweight on their BMI chart I didn't seem urgent enough to need help.

For almost a year we worked on my self-esteem, body image and breaking the binge/purge cycle. I had to unlearn so much about how I approached food, exercise and my body and relearn how to eat. Now I try to follow Intuitive Eating as much as possible, and when I find myself starting to criticise my body and how it looks, it helps me to remember everything it has done for me over the years, and that the way I look is the least interesting thing about myself. My relationship with my body is still a challenge, and some days it's harder than others, but when I look back to five years ago I can see how much progress I've made.

I contacted the Eating Disorders Association at around the same time as the CBT, who provide in-person and over-the-phone help, and they encouraged me to join their weekly support group. Like the AWARE groups, it was a powerful experience surrounded by others at different stages of recovery speaking openly about their struggles and realising I was never really alone. Any time I was struggling (which was a lot in the beginning), there was always an EDA volunteer on the other end of the phone or in the office I could talk things through with. They also had a support group for carers so mum could go and learn more about the illness, talk to others in the same situation and get advice. Soon after they helped to sign me up for eight weeks of the 'Tastelife' course run by Links Counselling which helps sufferers of eating disorders and their carers to understand their illness and move towards recovery. They also invited speakers from the BEAT UK charity and more locally The Lawrence Trust which specialises in supporting men with eating disorders and their loved ones. Things have improved a lot and the length of time now between binging and purging is increasing. It's something that I know I have to be aware of and continue to work at every day.

When I knew I was in a better place, I slowly started going back to work but turned down any long-term teaching opportunities, opting for day-to-day subbing instead. It meant I could slowly get back into the classroom without the same pressure or responsibility. However, going back to school with a clearer head helped me realise that teaching wasn't the vocation I wanted, so I applied to join the civil service instead. It was good timing because they were recruiting and now I feel happy and secure in my new career. It's good for me and my mind that at the end of the day I can close the laptop and won't have to think about work again until I log on the next morning.

Recovery was definitely not linear and it took several years before I felt confident that the depression was gone. Often it was one step forward, two steps back. I'm still in a form of therapy now called Emotional Freedom Therapy which uses a mix of meditation and tapping the body's meridian points to calm my mind and let go of fear. The EFT is also helping me to work on the rituals and thoughts I've developed since the hospital that initially were born from trying to get myself well, but now I can see are holding me back from trusting myself that I can cope day-to-day. Twice a year I meet with a psychiatrist to check-in, see if any new referrals need made and make sure the medication I'm on is still working. For some people antidepressants are temporary measures, stopped when they're in a better place. But as my doctor explained to me, mine is like a life jacket I wear to keep me bobbing along the surface and to stop me from going under again.

And although I'm in a good place, I'm well and my mood is stable, I still have days when I'm low or anxious, and I still occasionally have panic attacks. There are two things I tell myself on those days. The first is that instead of shutting out completely any of the sadder emotions and pretending they aren't there, I tell myself to feel them even if it's painful. I remind myself that every emotion is valid, they pass and it makes me human. The second comes from something I heard along the lines of 'you're as sick as your secrets' and it's true that once I tell someone the things I feel fearful of inside, they instantly become less powerful and intimidating.

But even so, with everything I've learnt about myself, on some of the more difficult days my mind can go straight to: everything would be easier if I was dead. But I know now that that is just a thought and an automatic response to stress or upset in my mind or body. I don't need to listen to it or act on it.

Now when my mood dips or my anxiety spikes, I try to stop, breathe and ask myself what's happening in my head right now. What exactly is making me feel this way? Usually I can pinpoint what it is and plan what I need to do to make it better. Some days I have to fight the urge to get into bed and pull the duvet over my head because I know that ultimately makes me feel worse. Instead I push myself to tell someone what I'm feeling and get it out in the open. Sometimes I need advice, but a lot of the time all I need is to say what I'm thinking out loud to realise I'm catastrophising or being too hard on myself. Other times it helps to write it down or go for a walk to think it all through. Sometimes I know that what I need to do is curl up on the sofa and allow myself to take it easy. It can take a few days, but it always passes.

I wouldn't say that I'm grateful for my depression, but I can appreciate that this struggle has taught me how to manage my mental health and I feel confident that I can handle whatever life and my brain might throw at me in the future. I know now that recovery is possible with the right help and I'm so grateful for the support, information and therapy I've been able to access since leaving the hospital. I've been able to let go of so much of the guilt and shame that I used to feel about my time as an in-patient and now releasing this diary feels like I can finally show myself that I have nothing to be ashamed of for becoming unwell.

Five years ago I couldn't see a way out of the depression that had taken over. I had an idea of what my life would be and I didn't think anything would ever change that. I'm so glad I was wrong.

Finally, I've found happiness, I've found peace and I'm excited for the future. If you're suffering, please reach out and ask for help. There is always hope.